In the Shadow of the Oak

JACK SCOLTOCK

I wish to see the Poorhouse looked to with dread by our labouring classes and the reproach for being an inmate of it extend downward from father to son. Let the poor see and feel that their parish, although it will not allow them to perish through absolute want, is yet the hardest taskmaster, the closest pay-master and the most harsh unkind friend they can apply to.

George Nicholls (1822)
Poor Law Commissioner

LONG TOWER

A Long Tower book from
GUILDHALL PRESS

First published in November 2003

Guildhall Press, Unit 15, Ráth Mór Centre,
Bligh's Lane, Derry BT48 0LZ
T: (028) 7136 4413 F: (028) 7137 2949
info@ghpress.com www.ghpress.com

Copyright© Jack Scoltock / Guildhall Press

ISBN 0 946451 75 3

All rights reserved

Cover and internal artwork by Marilyn McLaughlin
Typesetting and cover design by Kevin Hippsley and Joe McAllister

Supported by the Arts Council of Northern Ireland

This Project is supported by the European Union, administered by the
Local Strategy Partnership for the Derry City Council Area.

**EU Programme
for Peace and Reconciliation**
In Northern Ireland and the Border Regions of Ireland

**ARTS
COUNCIL**
of Northern Ireland

LOCAL STRATEGY PARTNERSHIP
DERRY CITY COUNCIL AREA

Acknowledgements

Special thanks to: Patrick Durnin (author of *The Workhouse and the Famine in Derry*), Paddy Gallagher, Matt Mulhern, Justine Scoltock, Marilyn McLaughlin, the Arts Council of Northern Ireland and the staff of Guildhall Press.

*To the unfortunates who had to seek succour
in the Derry Workhouse*

Contents

For Ursula with love

Emigration

The day his brother, Eamon, told him he was emigrating to America, Jake thought his whole world had collapsed, for he idolised his big brother.

That day, they were working in one of the long potato fields that ran down almost to the banks of the quarter-mile-wide, fast-flowing River Foyle. The brackish river wound its way through Derry to Lough Foyle and on to the Atlantic Ocean.

It was a dull, end-of-September day in Derry in 1871 and Jake and his brother were gathering potatoes behind their father, who was driving old Tom, a brown and white horse, up the muddy field. The sharp edge of the plough tore into the rich soil with a slushing sound, spewing the white, clay-spotted potatoes to the top. It was backbreaking work, but the brothers were well used to it. Jake, though only ten years old, was tall for his age. His brother was well built and a head-and-a-half taller. Both brothers had thick, brown curly hair, short stubby noses, and dark brown eyes. Clusters of freckles, evidence of that beautiful summer, covered Jake's face.

"Emigratin'!" Jake exclaimed, almost stopping.

His brother frowned and nodded at his father, who had his back to them, silently telling Jake to keep his voice down.

"But why?" whispered Jake.

Eamon shrugged. "There's a whole lot of reasons, Jake. I've made up me mind."

Jake's heart pounded against his ribs. Was it true? Was his brother really emigrating? He looked at his father's back as he whispered, "But what about Ann?" He hoped she was against it. Ann was Eamon's wife and they were expecting their first baby.

"Ann will go where I go," answered Eamon, wiping sweat from his mud-caked brow. "She's all fer it." He looked at his father's back again. "Jake," he whispered, "don't say anythin' to the oul' fella or me ma. I'm fer tellin' them the night."

It's true then, thought Jake, unable to stop a tear running down his face.

Realising his brother was upset, Eamon whispered, "Jake, luk, I ... I have to go. I ..."

"Will you two stop yappin' back there," growled their father, turning. "We need to get this crop gathered in by the morra. McConnell's expectin' the spuds bagged and stacked, ready fer market by the end of the week."

Charles McConnell owned the field and numerous other fields on the remote farm, several miles from Derry. He also owned the cottage Jake and his family lived in.

"Sorry, da," said Eamon.

***

The Miller family were Paddy, the father, a tall, thin man with brown hair streaked with grey, and Mary, his wife, a tiny, slender woman with dark hair and eyes to match. Eamon's wife, who lived with them, was a pleasant, round-faced girl with fair hair and blue eyes. Mr Miller and his two sons worked six days a week for the farmer and, in return, the Millers were paid ten shillings a week and had the cottage rent-free. Jake's father had once asked McConnell for an increase in pay, but McConnell, a gruff, burly man, told him that the right to live in the cottage could be deducted from their wages. Jake's father had never asked for a rise again.

***

As they worked their way up the field, Eamon thought about Ann and their decision to emigrate. She had argued at first, saying that his father couldn't work the fields on his own. Besides, she said, his mother would miss them. Jake would miss them. How could they cope? *"Don't ye think I know all that, Ann,"* he had cried. *"But we have to think about our lives now with the wain comin'. We can't live me ma and da's lives. Ah, luk,*

2

Ann, we'll do all right in America. I know we will. I know it. Sure when we get settled we can send fer them. I know me da will be against us goin', but he'll see reason."

By the end of the week, Ann was as convinced as he was that they should emigrate. The following week, they had walked into Derry and booked their passage. Now they had to tell Eamon's parents.

Working the rest of the day in the big field, Jake could hardly think of anything else. His brother was emigrating and, for the first time in his young life, he dreaded going back to the cottage.

Later, walking down the long, fuchsia-hedged lane to the cottage that lay in the lea of a low hill, Jake listened to his father and brother. "We should have all the spuds well in by four o'clock the morra," said Eamon.

"Aye, and in good time too," said his father, studying the sky. "The rain'll be here soon. God, the nights are fallin' fast, aren't they? Winter's just around the corner. I can feel it in me bones already."

"How's yer back the day, da?" asked Eamon.

His father took a few seconds before answering. "It's gran', aye, it's gran'."

Jake knew his father's back was far from grand. He had listened to his moans of pain the night before, after Eamon and Ann had gone out. Every evening, his mother massaged his father's back with a liniment she had concocted from flowers and axle grease scraped from the hub of a broken cartwheel that lay out in the back shed.

Changing the subject, Jake's father said, "I'm famished. There's nothin' like good hard sweat to work up an appetite, eh, son?" He slapped Eamon on the back, then pushed the rickety gate open.

Jake held back, watching his brother open the lower half of the front door and go inside. He sighed. He was dreading his dinner.

When he entered the cottage, he saw Eamon kiss Ann and smile. Jake's mother was already dishing out potato gruel into wooden bowls. The oak table at which they sat had been there when Jake's parents had first moved into the cottage. The top surface was scrubbed smooth, though one of the legs was short and rotted. A flat rock was wedged underneath the leg to keep it level. A jug of cold, spring-well water sat in the centre of the table, around which were four stools. Wooden spoons, one cup, two mugs, and a crockery jar were the only other items on the table. Jake's usual eating place was on a straw-filled cushion by the fire and, as he carried his bowl of gruel to the fireplace, he saw Eamon give Ann a look. Ann smiled at Jake as he passed, but he noticed her eyes hadn't the bright happiness in them they'd had when she'd told them all that she was pregnant.

When dinner was almost over, Jake's mother, noticing that Jake had hardly touched his food, asked, "Jake, what's the matter? Aren't ye feelin' well?" She knew her younger son loved his food and it was unusual for him not to be finished long before everyone else.

"Aye, ma," said Jake. "I'm all right." He glanced at Eamon.

"Don't waste yer food, son," said his father. "There are some who'd nearly kill ye fer what's in that bowl."

Jake frowned. "What do ye mean, da?"

"The Workhouse, that's what I mean. There are many livin' in there who are half-starved and half-dead who'd give anythin' fer a bowl of gruel."

The Workhouse? thought Jake. It was the first time he had heard the word. "Is that a house where they work, da?" he asked.

His father looked at Jake's mother and laughed. She smiled. But his father grew suddenly serious. "Naw, son; not where they work ... well, they do. Ach, it's a terrible place where unfortunates end up that have nowhere to live, or food to eat. Count yersel' lucky ye've a hard-workin' family around ye and enough food to eat."

Jake looked at Eamon, then back at his father. "Da," he asked, "do you think we'll end up in the Workhouse?"

"Not likely, son. We're lucky enough to have a roof over our heads ..."

"Lucky!" exclaimed Eamon. "How's that, da? We're only allowed to live in this cottage because McConnell owns us ..."

4

"Owns us!" exclaimed his father, his face darkening with anger. "No-one owns a Miller. Remember that, boy. No-one."

"Well, McConnell owns our home. We've nothin' only the work," snapped Eamon. Jake's heartbeat quickened. He could feel the tenseness building already.

"Nothin'?" said his father, raising his hand to indicate everyone. "We've each other, haven't we?" Eamon gave Ann a look again.

Jake saw his mother frown. She had caught the look that had passed between them. "What is it, Eamon?" she asked. Jake's mother could always tell when there was something wrong. Jake had heard his father once say she had the sixth sense.

Eamon looked at Ann again. "It's ... it's ... Philadelphia." He blurted out the word.

Now it was his father who frowned. "Don't tell me yer goin' to start on about America again," he said. "I thought all that talk was over and done with."

"Ach, da," said Eamon, rising from the table. "Ye'd better know now. Ann and me have decided. We're emigratin' to Philadelphia next week. We've already booked our passage."

Jake's heart pounded against his ribs like small explosions when his father suddenly rose from the table, causing the stool he had been sitting on to skitter across the floor and hit the wall.

"Philadelphia!" he shouted. "That's all it is these days! If it was such a great place there'd be no-one left in Derry! They'd all be out there, in bloody Philadelphia ..."

"Paddy," began Mary.

"Da, don't ye understand why Ann and me have to go?" said Eamon. "What's here fer us? Luk at you, me ma, all of us. We work McConnell's farm six days a week and what have we got to show fer it? Nothin'. Bloody nothin'. McConnell owns us. Aye, da, he does. He owns us. We're his slaves, to do with what he wants. We own nothin'. He only has to threaten us with eviction and we do anythin' he wants. We own nothin'," he repeated, looking around the room. "We don't even own this ... this hovel we call a home."

"Eamon," exclaimed his mother. "It's God's will we live this way."

"God's will!" snapped Eamon. "Ma, catch yersel' on."

Jake gasped. He had never heard Eamon raise his voice to his mother or turn a word in her mouth.

"Ma," said Eamon, lowering his voice. "It's God's will that Ann and me are goin' to Philadelphia. In America we have a chance to better oursel's. In Philadelphia, there's opportunity, work, aye, and plenty of it. Good money fer them that are willin' to work hard to get it. Philadelphia is ..."

"Enough!" roared his father, banging the table with his fist. A cup and a bowl bounced to the floor. "I don't want to hear any more about Philadelphia! No more! Do ye hear me?" He glared at Eamon.

"Paddy, Eamon's right," said Ann quietly. "Luk at us. We barely have enough to eat. I want my baby to have a better life than the one I've had so far. I want my baby to have a better future. In America, there's more opportunity. There's a future fer Eamon and me." She paused before adding, "At least there's hope."

Jake's father frowned. "There's always hope, girl," he muttered.

"Aye, well, there's no hope here," snapped Eamon. "No hope of anythin' resemblin' a decent future ..."

Jake gave a start when his father banged the table again. "Tell us!" he shouted. "What would yees do out there? What would yees do if, God ferbid, anythin' were to happen to Ann?" He looked at Ann. "Ye'd be among strangers, aye, strangers." He turned to glare at Eamon. "Who could yees turn to? Who could yees trust? No-one. No-one would give a damn about yees. At least here yees have yer family and friends. I can't turn to *my* family if anything goes wrong. They all died in the Famine. Me sister and two brothers. Me da. Think about that!"

"Luk, da," said Eamon quietly. "We'll be all right. Ach, da, can't ye see why we have to go? Ann will be havin' the wain soon. I don't want it growin' up here ..."

"What's wrong with here?" shouted his father. "It was good enough fer ye before."

"Aye," said Eamon. "Maybe it was. But now I want somethin' better fer me and Ann. I don't want to work here all me life just to exist. I don't want to ... to be ... like you."

His father gaped at him, the mixture of hurt and anger showing in his eyes.

"Da," explained Eamon. "Ye've worked here all yer life and what have ye to show fer it?"

"You!" roared his father. "I have you and Jake to show fer it." All of a sudden he sighed and bent over the table, leaning his fists on it.

Jake studied his father. All the energy seemed to have drained from his body. It was the first time Jake realised his father was getting old. He had never thought about it before, but his father seemed suddenly to have aged.

"I'll get some turf in," said Jake's mother, quietly rising to go to the fire for the basket.

"I'll get it, ma," offered Jake, wanting to get outside and away from the quarrelling.

"No, son, it's all right. I'll get it," said his mother, smiling at him. Everyone watched as she went to the door.

Outside, Jake's mother reached for a long piece of turf. She shook the dry dust from it before placing it in the basket. Before bending for another piece, she glanced in the window. As she did, she listened to the raised voices inside. "So it's come," she whispered.

She had noticed the change in Eamon ever since Ann had told them she was pregnant. She had noticed his restlessness. "They're goin' away," she choked as the tears rolled down her face. But suddenly she wiped at her eyes with the back of her hand. It wouldn't do to let them see she was crying.

As she bent for another piece of turf, she thought about Paddy. He would argue and shout, but she knew Eamon wouldn't heed him. He was stubborn, like his father, and strong. Paddy had been strong once, and full of life. She had loved him the first time she had seen him. She remembered the time he had thrashed her two brothers who had objected to him calling on her. Her father, too, had objected to their marriage. She had been glad to get away from her family with a man she loved and have a cottage of their own. Her life there had been one of drudgery until Paddy came one night for her, breaking down the door and taking her away. She hadn't always been happy with Paddy. It was a hard life. She'd had two miscarriages before Jake had been born. "Jake," she whispered. "He'll be lonely. I'll be lonely ..." and suddenly she was crying again.

"Ye'll break yer mother's heart if ye emigrate. Ye know that, don't ye?" said Eamon's father.

At this, Ann began to cry. Tears brimmed Eamon's eyes as he croaked, "Da, don't ye think I know that?" His voice hardened. "But we're still goin'. It's hard on us, hard on all of us, but we've made up our minds. We're emigratin'. In America, we'll have a decent life. We'll be able to hold our heads high. Here, we're cowed down, workin' our guts out fer McConnell. He's the only one benefitin' from our labour, not us. In America, every man is regarded as equal. We'll all have an equal chance to become a success."

"America," spat Jake's father, as if the word was a sour gooseberry. "Curse the place. I hate the very sound of it. It's drainin' the very life's blood from Ireland with its false promises. It's ..."

Just then, Jake's mother returned. Jake dived to help her with the basket and they carried it to the fireplace. As his mother placed a piece of turf on the fire, she realised Ann was crying. Dusting her hands on her dress, she went over to her. "Ann," she said softly. "Don't be upsettin' yersel'. Ye'll only disturb yer wain." She patted her daughter-in-law's hand.

"Ach, Mary," said Jake's father. "It's all this talk of emigratin'. Can't ye talk some sense into them?"

Jake's mother frowned as she turned to look at him. "Paddy, ye can't blame them fer wantin' somethin' better nor this," she said quietly. Turning back to Ann, she said, "But I wish ye'd wait, Ann, 'til yer wain is born. That would be the sensible thing to do."

"They don't want to do the sensible thing," snapped Paddy. "Fer God's sake, Eamon, would ye lissen to sense – goin' to Philadelphia. Yees mightn't even reach the place. How many ships these past years have ye heard of that has foundered on the way? Some of them sank before they even left the mouth of the Foyle. Luk what happened to yer Uncle Jim and his wife and wain, and three years ago to the McLaughlin family. Remember

Johnny McLaughlin? We met him in Derry once. Aye, him, his wife, and their eight wains. They set off to Baltimore, or some place like that. They all drowned. Their youngest wain was eight months old. What a waste of life! The whole family gone. They had high hopes fer the future, high hopes and a better life. Hah! They've no life now."

"Well, at least they tried fer a better life," said Eamon, turning to Ann. "If Ann and me stayed here now, we'd always regret it. We'd have given up. There'd be no life fer us. We'd be better off dead. Da, can't ye see what I'm on about? What sort of life would our wain have here in this place? Our nearest neighbours are miles away, and this cottage is overcrowded as it is ..."

"We could make room," began his father. "We ..."

Suddenly, there was a knock at the door. Jake hurried to open it, glad that whoever it was had come just in time to stop the row. He opened the top half of the door, wincing with pain from the blister that had burst in the centre of his hand earlier that day.

Four people were standing there. Jake recognised them. It was James Carlin, a tall, well-built man with fair hair, a bronzed face and a broken nose. His wife Kathleen, a busty, handsome, red-haired woman, and Thomas Quinn, a red-curly-haired slim man with a freckled face. Beside him stood his girlfriend, Bridget. She was reed-thin with a sharp nose and her black hair was cut short.

James pushed gently past Jake when he opened the lower half of the door and, as he closed it behind them, Jake heard James say, as he handed Eamon a jug of poitín, "We called round to give yees a good send off. I couldn't let yees go off to America without a drink inside yees, now, could I?" Rubbing his hands, he went over to the fire. "How are ye, Mr Miller, Mrs Miller? God, but yees are lukin' well. Life's been good to yees."

Eamon's father scowled but said nothing.

"Here, James," said Eamon. "Sit here. Kathleen, sit over there by Ann. Bridget, you and Thomas will have to stand." He looked at his father as he added, "There's not enough seats to go round." He smiled at James. "I didn't think I'd get to see any of yees before we went."

"Some hope of that," said James. He nodded to the jug. "Are

ye goin' to save that? It could go bad before the night's over. Ha-ha, ha-ha." Jake liked James. Once, when he had visited after Eamon's wedding, he had given Jake a penny. He still had it.

"Jake, would ye hand me those mugs and that cup and jar," said his mother. "I'll give them a wash out."

As Jake bent to pick up one of the mugs, he heard James say, "Well, Eamon, it won't be long now 'til yer off."

"Aye, Eamon," said Thomas. "How long is it?"

Eamon glanced at his father. "Five more days." His father gave a start. "I didn't think I'd get to see yees before ..." Eamon began to say again.

"Did ye think I'd let the best man at me weddin' go off to a strange land without a fire in his belly?" exclaimed James, smiling. "God, five days, eh? Five days and you and Ann will be off to start a new life."

A few seconds later, Jake's mother came back from the scullery with the washed containers. Jake watched as Eamon passed round the drink. He wondered what poitín tasted like.

"God, Eamon, how I envy ye!" said James after taking a sip. "Just think, in six weeks, maybe less, ye'll be in America. The wonder of travel, eh?"

"Aye, the wonder of travel," muttered Jake's father, and Jake saw him gulp the poitín down, then reach and pour some more into his mug. Jake glanced at his mother and saw her frown.

"Ye must be lukin' forward to it, Ann," said Kathleen.

Ann smiled. "I've mixed feelin's about it. I'm both scared and excited all at the same time. I hope the journey isn't too rough, though. I've been gettin' sick a lot these past weeks."

"Ah, sure ye'll be gran'," said Thomas. "I tell ye, I wish I was goin' with yees. What an adventure! A new life, new faces. A new wain." He smiled. "New wains, American wains. Eamon, yer wains will be Americans. What an adventure! Aye, I wish I was goin' with yees."

"Thomas Quinn," snapped Bridget. "What sort of an adventurer would ye make? Ye'd nearly get lost in yer own house."

James, Eamon and Kathleen laughed, but Jake couldn't find anything funny to laugh at. His brother was going away. Jake thought he would never laugh again.

"Thomas," said Eamon, "ye could come over later, ye know. When Ann and me get set up, we could put ye up 'til ye get a job."

Jake saw Bridget give a start and her lips tightened. Thomas glanced at her. "Ah, sure, Eamon, ye know me ma's not well. I couldn't leave her now. She's got far worse since me da passed away." He glanced at Bridget again. "There's just the two of us now, me ma and me. At least," he said, looking at Eamon's parents, "yer ma and da's in good health." He smiled as he raised the jar. "Here's to yer good health, folks ..."

"A lotta good our health will be to us if they go," snapped Paddy and then took another long drink. This time he coughed as the strong liquor caught the back of his throat.

"We all have to let go sometime, Mr Miller," said James.

Suddenly, Paddy rose to his feet. "Let go!" he shouted, the veins standing out on his brow. "What the blazes have *you* to let go? Why don't *you* go to America if it's such a great bloody place? Or is *yer* ma sick too?"

"Da!" shouted Eamon. "Fer God's sake, what way's that to talk?"

"Well, they all have their excuses!" shouted his father. "They say they'd like to emigrate, but they won't. What's wrong with Derry, anyway?"

"Mr Miller, don't get me wrong," said James quietly. "As far as I'm concerned, there's no place like Derry. But life here is hard; money's tight. Ye need money and land, and America's the place to get it ..."

"I heard about a man from Strabane who emigrated to America two years ago," interrupted Thomas. "They say he has over a hundred men workin' fer him – some transport business, I believe. That's where the money is. Transport."

"And what about the man ye heard about, James?" said Kathleen.

"From Sion Mills. Aye. They say he's a millionaire now."

"They say he owns a big house with fifty servants," added Kathleen. "Fifty servants. Imagine that."

"I heard about him," said Thomas. "They say he's married to a senator's daughter out there."

11

Jake had been studying his father through all this. A vein on the side of his neck bulged and looked about to burst. Suddenly, "Lissen to yees!" his father roared. "Would yees lissen to yersel's. They say this, and they say that. So far, I've seen no proof of anybody ever comin' back from America with their pockets full of gold. Tell us," he snapped, glaring at James, "have ye any proof of anythin' ye've heard? Has any one of ye known anyone to come back from America any better off than when they left Ireland?"

"Well," said James, looking at Kathleen, "not me personally, Mr Miller. But Kathleen here has. Her cousin Jack wrote to her once. He says there's loads of work out there fer them that wants it. Isn't that right, Kathleen?"

"Aye, it is. Jack says he's workin' in a place called Virginia. He's in charge of over two hundred black men on a plantation. That's a kind of big farm, I think."

"Huh!" said Jake's father. "Some way, that, to make a livin'. Takin' advantage of the poor critturs. What sort of a man would take a job like that? What sort of a man would drive the poor blacks into the ground?" He turned to Eamon. "And you talk about *us* bein' cowed down. The poor blacks in America are far worse off."

"Da," hissed Eamon. "The blacks are free now to work fer who they like. Luk, can't ye be a bit more civil?"

"Ah," said James, "sure I understand how yer da feels ..."

"Ye do, do ye!" roared Eamon's father. "How in hell do ye? Have you an eldest son goin' off to a place over three thousand miles away? Have you a son and his pregnant wife goin' away, never to come back again?" He swung to Eamon. "Have ye thought about that? Aye, we'll never see ye again. Never see you, nor Ann, nor our grandchild. Have ye thought about that?"

Jake suddenly felt the tears sting his eyes and swallowed several times trying to keep from crying. He hadn't thought about it.

"Paddy, don't," Jake's mother said quietly. "Eamon and Ann have their own lives to live. We can't keep them tied to us. Eamon has Ann now and soon, God willin', a wain to luk after.

Paddy, they've made up their minds." She sighed. "They've booked their passage. We'll just have to accept it."

Paddy frowned deeply. "Ye know ye'll miss them, Mary," he whispered.

Jake gulped as a tear trickled down his face, and his mother, who was near to tears herself, said, "Aye, Paddy, I'll miss them." At this, Ann began to cry again.

"Ah, it's all right, Ann," said Mary, going to her. "I know yees have to go. Yees are young. Yees need a life. I know there's not much here fer yees. Things will never change here." She looked at her husband. "We've grown old before our time and we'll work 'til we drop. Then," she added, almost in a whisper, "someone else will take our place."

"Aye," said her husband bitterly, "we'll work 'til we drop. Then what's left fer us? McConnell will evict us. Then what'll be left fer us? The Workhouse, that's what. The curse of the poor and unfortunate. Aye!" he shouted at Eamon. "The Derry Workhouse!"

"Da, ye know I'd never let that happen. If yer ever in trouble, just get word to James or Bridget. They can write to me. I'll get money to ye. I'll send enough fer all of yees to join me and Ann. As soon as we get settled I'll ..."

His father scowled as he snapped, "I'll never set foot in that damned country."

"Ach, da," said Eamon. "Don't try to make us feel worse about emigratin'." His eyes filled with tears. "Da, don't ye want us to have a better life?"

Sighing, his father sat down heavily. With a sniff, he looked at Eamon. "Aye, son," he croaked. "I do. I really do. But yer goin' away and ... and ..." He pushed his head into his hands.

Ann began to cry again.

"Here, Mr Miller," said James quickly. "Have another drink ..."

"James," said Mary. "I think there's been enough drinkin' done the night." She turned to Ann. "Ann, love, would ye like to help me get our visitors somethin' to eat?"

"I'll give ye a hand, too," said Kathleen, rising.

The women went out to the scullery. Jake noticed Thomas looking after Bridget. When she was gone, Thomas said,

"Eamon, me ma's only an excuse not to emigrate. To tell ye the truth, I'm too much of a coward. I really admire you and Ann."

"So do I," said James. "But I suppose I'm the lucky one, when ye think about it. I've piles of work. There's more new shirt factories goin' up every day. If the work keeps up, I'll never leave Derry."

"Ye do right," said Jake's father. "A tradesman like you will never be outta work." He looked at Eamon. "If ye had a trade, ye wouldn't have to emigrate."

"Aye, but da, that's just it, I have a trade. And it's thanks to you." His father frowned. So did Jake. "I know the land," explained Eamon. "I know how to grow things. You taught me. They say in America the climate's more suited to growin' wheat."

"Wheat!" snapped his father. "The money's in spuds. It's not like the famine days any more. Spuds, that's what to grow."

"Yer right, there, Mr Miller," said James. "Spuds is the things to be growin' all right." At this, Eamon stared at James with a look as if to say, whose side are you on anyway? "Well, I mean, we eat the things, don't we?" said James quickly.

"We eat bread, too," snapped Eamon.

"Ach, son," exclaimed his father. "Why don't ye lissen to sense? Stay here. We'll all manage somehow. Ann will soon have her ..."

"Da!" shouted Eamon. "Have ye not been lissenin'? Can't ye see I won't change me mind? Ann and me are emigratin'. It's been decided. We've booked our passage. We're goin'."

"It's not been decided!" exclaimed his father, standing up again. "Ye can change yer mind, can't ye?" He scowled. "If ye go, ye'll go without my blessin'. I'll not be seein' ye off."

Eamon's face darkened. "Aye, well, da, you do whatever ye like. You do whatever ye like."

Jake stared at his brother and father. It was the first time he had ever seen them so angry with each other. He tried to understand why Eamon was going. He could understand now why his father was so upset. He was fighting to keep Eamon here. He, too, wanted to scream at Eamon to stay. He was upset. He'd miss Eamon. He'd have no-one to talk to.

***

That night, he listened to Ann crying and Eamon trying to pacify her. Jake's own tears soaked his straw-filled pillow as he silently cried himself to sleep.

Later still, he had a nightmare. A great black building suddenly loomed out of the mist and he was passing through the mist towards a black door. As the door opened, he heard the terrible crying and moans from inside. Now he could see the ghostly faces of young boys. Their black, staring eyes followed him inside as they cried, "GO BACK! DON'T COME IN! GO BACK!"

"Ahhhh!" Jake woke, shivering, and lay awake until dawn when he rose, with a terrible foreboding, to another day of hard work in the fields.

EAMON'S FAREWELL

On Saturday, Eamon and Ann, accompanied by Jake and his mother, headed off to board the ship at Derry Quay. It was a dark, wet morning and Jake walked silently beside his mother. He was carrying one of his brother's cloth bags. As they trudged through the rain, he thought about his father.

Paddy had stubbornly refused to go with them. Jake had stood at the gate with Ann and his mother, watching as Eamon pleaded with his father to come with them and see them off. But Paddy, who hadn't spoken to Eamon since their quarrel, glared at him, then just turned and walked back into the cottage and slammed the door. They had all cried when Eamon, with tears running down his face, had pleaded, *"Da, please! Please come with us ..."* But all they heard was the bar crash into place as Paddy locked the top door.

***

It took them almost an hour and a half to reach Derry and, as they headed across the new Carlisle Bridge, they saw some factory girls, late for work, hurrying towards Tillie and Henderson's shirt factory. As they walked down John Street to the quay, they saw a few other people, some of them carrying bags and wooden chests, proceeding in the same direction. When they reached the quay, about two hundred people were already there, standing alongside the ship that would carry the emigrants to Philadelphia.

The wooden ship bounced and lifted as the muddy waters of the Foyle threatened to tear it from the thick hemp ropes that held it to three squat wooden bollards evenly placed alongside the vessel.

As Jake, his mother, brother and sister-in-law approached the ship, a bell rang and, looking up, Jake saw a rangy cabin boy ringing a polished brass bell. Jake sighed silently, the hollow feeling in his stomach growing worse as they edged along the slippery green quay to the bottom of the narrow gangway. He sniffed back a tear as he bent and placed the bag he carried at Eamon's feet. Now they all looked at his mother.

Suddenly, croaking unintelligibly, Ann threw her arms around Mary's shoulders and pulled her close. Jake saw his mother stiffen, but her thin hands reached to touch Ann's shoulders lightly. Looking over her shoulders, Ann tried to smile at Jake, but her face contorted as the tears ran down her cheeks. Then, when she hugged Jake close, she whispered, "Luk after her, Jake." Suddenly, she was crying again and stumbling up the gangway.

Everyone watched her until she reached the top. Then Eamon turned to his mother. His face looked drawn and pale, and Jake almost cried out when he forced a smile at her. Awkwardly, his brother reached to hug his mother, whispering in choking breaths as the tears spilled down his handsome face, "Don't worry about me and Ann, ma. We'll be all right. As soon ... as soon as I get settled, I'll send ye some money."

Jake couldn't cry as he watched his mother hug Eamon for the last time. He was all cried out. His brother was going away, really emigrating, and he would never see him again.

Now, with tears and rain soaking his face, Eamon turned to Jake. He reached to shake Jake's hand. But suddenly, with a cry, Jake had his arms wrapped around his waist and was crying into his chest. "Don't go, Eamon," he cried. "Stay. Please. Please, don't go. Please."

Just then, the cabin boy rang the bell again. This time he sang out in a high-pitched voice, "All aboard fer Philadelphy, Amerikay! All aboard that's goin' aboard. Ship sails in three minutes. All aboard that's goin' aboard!" He rang the bell again, its heart-tugging peal followed by the crying and frenzied hugging from some of the other people crowded around the Millers.

"I'll have to go," whispered Eamon, gently forcing Jake away.

Jake saw his mother force a smile and she said quietly, "Aye, son, ye have to go."

Looking past his brother to the ship, Jake saw Ann watching them from the deck. He waved with an arm that felt as heavy as lead. Ann waved back.

Now Eamon bent and lifted his bags. He gulped as he looked at his mother and brother for the last time. "I'd better get on board, ma," he croaked. Suddenly he was crying and, dropping his bags, he reached to hug his mother and Jake again. As Jake held Eamon, he could feel his heart pounding against his ear. Then he heard his mother give a huge sigh as Eamon suddenly released them and, still crying, he grabbed his bags and ran up the gangway.

Jake's mother still stood with her arms outstretched as other people pushed past her to climb the gangway.

The bell rang again. "All aboard! All aboard fer Philadelphy, Amerikay! Ship sails in one minute. All aboard fer Philadelphy. Ship sails in one minute. All aboard that's stayin' aboard!"

Philadelphia, thought Jake as he moved out of the way to watch other crying people run onto the gangway. Philadelphia, a place that would welcome his brother and his wife. He wished he were going with them.

Now, as the crewmen pulled in the starboard rope, he felt the hot tears running down his face and he found himself huddling close to his mother at the front of the crowd, waving. The ship eased slowly away from the quay. Soon, it was picking up speed as it headed down the fast-flowing Foyle.

As they watched the ship sail away, the rain stopped. The black clouds that had hung over the Donegal hills all morning were quickly breaking up; shadows stretched down along the fields below them as the sun struggled to make it a day.

Jake and his mother still waved, even as the ship sailed around the bend of the river and out of sight. Gradually, the people began to head for home and soon Jake and his mother were standing alone.

Shortly, with a heavy sigh, his mother turned to him and whispered, "Come on, Jake. Let's go home. Yer father will be waitin'."

The rain began again half an hour after they left Derry and, by the time they reached the cottage, they were soaked. Jake's father was standing at the door. When he looked past them and saw Eamon wasn't there, he turned and went inside.

For the second time in his young life, Jake hated going inside the cottage. When he did, he saw his father standing by the fire, staring into it.

"So, he's gone," his father said quietly.

"Aye," said Jake's mother, "they're gone."

His father sighed deeply. Then, rising, he reached for his coat. "Come on, Jake," he said quietly, "we've some fencin' to sort out before the winter sets in."

Jake glanced at his mother and then he followed his father outside. As he was about to pass the window, he glanced inside. He could see his mother bent over the table, crying. Sniffing back his own tears, he followed his father up the lane.

***

Now the cottage seemed so empty. The silence between his mother and father was awful. Their hurt was tearing them apart. Jake could understand how they felt, but there was no-one to help him with his loss and he kept his hurt to himself. For the next three nights, he cried himself to sleep.

***

A few days after they had finished work on the top field, Jake and his father were taking old Tom in to the blacksmith to have one of his hooves seen to when they met McConnell and his eldest son, Samuel. Samuel was a smaller version of his father – and equally unpleasant. The McConnells were driving a cart full of hay to the big barn.

"I hear yer eldest has emigrated, Miller," said McConnell, studying Jake.

"Aye, sir," said Jake's father, tipping his head in salute.

"Well, I hope ye can cope with the extra work his absence is bound to cause," said the farmer.

"Oh, we can, sir," said Jake's father. "No need to worry, sir."

The farmer scowled. "I'm not worried, Miller. You're the one who should be worryin'." He took a long look at Jake, and then drove away.

Extra work, thought Jake, remembering how hard Eamon had worked. He studied his father. He was staring after the McConnells. There and then, Jake knew they would never be able to do the work of three. Without Eamon's help, they were in trouble.

AN ACCIDENT

Eamon woke early. The sun was streaming through one of the four narrow windows in the small barn where they lived. During his spare time, and with the help of two Irish farm hands, Eamon had converted the barn into fairly comfortable living accommodation for himself, Ann and their baby son, Patrick. The low wooden barn ran adjacent to three 2-storey barns that lay parallel with the main ranch house. Several of the farm hands lived in one of these barns in rougher conditions than the Millers. None of them was married, and it was only because Ann had been expecting that Eamon had been allowed to use the small barn as temporary living quarters. The farm and over two thousand acres of arable land belonged to Jack Cartwright and his wife. The Cartwrights had lost their only son in a tragic farm accident eight years earlier.

Ann yawned and, rubbing the sleep from one eye, she looked at her husband. Eamon was looking into the small cot and cooing softly at Patrick, who had been born four months earlier. The baby gurgled happily as Eamon whispered, "How are we today, wee man, eh?" Smiling, he rubbed Patrick's left cheek with the thick knuckle of his forefinger.

"Yer up early!" exclaimed Ann, suddenly yawning as she slipped out of bed. "I'll feed him first; then I'll get breakfast." She frowned. Eamon appeared not to have heard her. He was staring thoughtfully down at Patrick. "What is it, Eamon?" she asked. "Eamon?"

"What?" He turned.

"What were ye thinkin' about?"

"How did ye ..." He smiled. Ann always knew. "Ach, I was just thinking it would be great if Jake was here. There's piles of work fer him. He'd make somethin' of his life here. Mr Cartwright

21

will need more men soon. Me da should be here as well, and me ma, all of them."

Ann sighed and then went to him. Placing her soft hands one on each side of his bronzed face, she kissed him softly and said, "Even if they were here, Eamon, where would they live? There's no room here. Besides," she added, taking Eamon's left hand and placing it on her stomach, "there will be four of us soon."

Eamon frowned. "Four of us? What do ye mean?"

Ann smiled.

Eamon gasped. "Ye mean ..."

She nodded.

"Four of us," cried Eamon, tears brimming his eyes.

***

Three weeks later, he stood with Mr Cartwright on the edge of one of the three 40-acre fields that lay near the foot of a low mountain about two miles from the farm. Cartwright had called him over. The boss was a tall, silver-haired man with tanned, leathery skin and grey eyes. He had a pleasant face, but Eamon and the other hands knew he could be hard when it was required. Cartwright wore a checked blue shirt and thick cotton trousers. His shirtsleeves were rolled halfway up his muscled arms. Eamon and all the men admired the boss. He wasn't afraid to pitch in when they were behind with gathering in the wheat and the other crops.

"We're well behind with the big fields," said Cartwright, studying him. "We'll need men sooner than I thought, and we'll need more before spring comes. They'll have to be steady men, too. I want no casual labour. What do you think, Eamon?"

Eamon raised his eyebrows. He was surprised, for it was the first time the boss had asked his opinion about anything. Looking towards the far side of the field, where some of the men were working, he said, "Ye could use three, maybe four, men now to finish the wheat before autumn, sir. And I would think ye'll need at least another three, maybe four, by the spring.

Aye," he said, "at least another three now. They should carry us through to autumn."

Cartwright smiled. There was quite a lot about Eamon that reminded him of his own son. "Eamon," he said, "would you like to accompany me into town on Saturday night for a beer or two? We could keep an eye out for some likely men."

"Saturday night, sir?" said Eamon. Was the boss really asking him to go for a beer with him? "Aye," he said quickly, "Saturday night would be fine, sir."

Cartwright smiled. "Eamon, do I call you sir, or Mr Miller?" Eamon frowned. "No, sir."

"Well, call me Jack then. I'd feel comfortable with that." Cartwright smiled again and said, "I'll call for you on Saturday, then."

"Aye, sir, er ... Jack," said Eamon as he watched Cartwright walk to the cart with its two horses hitched to a pole nearby and drive off down the rough track road.

***

That Saturday, as they drove back from town, Eamon glanced into the back of the cart. Two men lay slumped in sleep. Another lay in a stupor on his back, staring up at the starry sky. Eamon and the boss had chosen the three men from a group of seven.

"They look like they'll be hard workers," said Cartwright, nodding back at the cart.

"If they aren't, they'll soon learn to be," said Eamon, smiling. He felt in good spirits. The night in town with the boss had been less of a dread than he'd thought. He had enjoyed himself.

Cartwright smiled back. "How are you getting on in the barn?" he asked.

"Fine, sir, er ... Jack. Ann's expectin' again," he said quickly.

Cartwright pulled lightly on the reins and the horses slowed. "Good," he said. "Congratulations."

"Thanks," said Eamon as they picked up speed again. A few minutes later he said, "Sir ... Jack?"

"Yeah?"

"There's a house near town Ann and me would like to buy."

"A house?"

"Aye. The barn is fine fer now, but Ann will need more space when the new wain comes. The house we've luked at would suit us." Eamon took a deep breath before speaking. "If I worked the rest day fer two years, I could pay fer it."

Cartwright frowned. "Work the rest day? I don't like ..."

Eamon took a long deep breath before saying, "Jack, I was wonderin' if ye could see yer way to lendin' us the deposit. The owners of the house need a deposit if they're goin' to hold it fer us, and I could work the rest day and pay ye back."

Cartwright flicked at the roan on the right, and the horses picked up speed. It was a while before he spoke, and Eamon was now regretting he had asked the boss for the loan. Maybe it's spoiled what little friendship we had, he thought.

"Eamon," said Cartwright suddenly. "You're a good worker, a hard worker, the best I have. You're good with the crops. I was thinking. With the three new men and the men we'll need, come spring, I'll need a foreman to keep them at it. I can't be everywhere all of the time. I'll need someone I can trust." He turned and looked directly into Eamon's eyes. "Can I trust you, Eamon?"

Eamon's heart pounded. "Ye know ye can," he answered.

Cartwright smiled. "Yeah," he said flicking his whip at the white horse, "I know I can, Eamon. But I don't like any of the hands working the rest day. Every worker needs time to rest and play, remember that."

"Yes, sir ... Jack."

They rode the rest of the way in silence. An hour later, they reached the ranch house. As Eamon and the boss watched the new men unhitch the horses, Cartwright said, "Eamon, would you like to bring Ann and your baby to dinner tomorrow? I'm sure my wife would be glad of the company."

"Aye," said Eamon, "Ann would be glad of the company as well. Thanks." He stared after Jack as he walked towards the ranch house. When the horses were settled and the men shown to their quarters, he hurried to tell Ann all that had happened.

The following week, Eamon and Ann lodged a deposit on the house with a lawyer from town. And yet, though everything was going well for them, Eamon missed his family. They should be here, he thought. This is the life they should have. They should be here.

***

That long, hard winter, and right through the cold spring and wet summer, Jake and his parents worked together, somehow managing to do the exhausting work McConnell asked of them. Many a night they staggered home, soaked to the skin, too tired to even eat. And all the time, Paddy's back was getting worse. Jake knew they couldn't go on like this for much longer.

In the middle of November, a few days after an early shower of snow, McConnell called. "I'll need ye both over at the farmhouse the night," he said. "I've taken delivery of that new cartwheel and I'll need yer help to put it on." He studied Jake's father. "You all right, Miller?" he asked.

"Aye, fine, sir," said Jake's father, frowning. When McConnell left, he said to Mary, "What did he mean, am I all right?"

Mary glanced at Jake, then said to her husband, "Ach, he's just bein' his usual ignorant self, Paddy."

Jake looked away, for he knew why McConnell had asked if his father was all right. His father wasn't looking all right. The pain in his back was getting worse every day, and he looked haggard.

Four hours later, by the light of two oil lamps, Jake, his father and Samuel were levering one side of the cart upright. A heavy barrel filled with sand was jammed against the inside of the greased axle, and a long wooden beam was laid across it. On a command from the farmer, the three hauled down on the beam and slowly the cart rose level. McConnell rolled the cartwheel into position, ready to tap it onto the axle. Raising a wooden hammer, he swung it at the hub of the wheel. The crack echoed around the yard, but the wheel proved to be tight.

"Hold on, da," said Samuel suddenly. "I'll get some grease ..."
But the instant he released the beam, the sudden extra weight

Jake and his father had to hold took them by surprise. With a cry, Jake was thrown one way and his father the other as the beam was twisted out of their grip. The cartwheel spun away as the cart crashed to the ground on its side.

"You stupid fools!" roared McConnell, who had leapt to safety just in time.

"It was yer son's fault!" shouted Jake as he scrambled to his feet. He glared at Samuel. "He let go." It was then he heard his father groan. Quickly, he turned and bent to help him to his feet. "Da, are ye all right?" he whispered.

"You all right, Miller?" asked the farmer, narrowing his eyes as he studied Jake's father.

"Ay ... aye, sir," gasped Paddy. Jake studied his father. He could see in the dull light he wasn't all right. He was hurt. His father frowned at him and shook his head, telling him silently to say nothing. "Just a wee twist, sir," he said.

Before long, with Samuel's help, they had lifted the cart into position again. The end of the axle had been heavily greased and, with a few hard taps, the wheel was soon in position. McConnell then sent Jake to the barn for one of three horses he owned, besides old Tom, and soon the horse was fixed to the cart. After a few runs up and down the long lane to the farmhouse, McConnell was satisfied that the cartwheel was running and secure. A few minutes later, he dismissed Jake and his father. As they walked down the path for home, McConnell studied Jake's father. Paddy was limping.

When they were almost out of sight of the farmer and his son, Jake glanced back. In the lamplight, he could see both McConnells watching them.

When they reached the road, out of view of the farm, Jake whispered, "Da, are ye really all right?" His father didn't answer, but suddenly, with a groan, he sank to his knees and rolled over onto his side. "Da!" shouted Jake.

"It's bad, son," gasped his father. "I've done somethin' in."

Aghast, Jake bent beside him. He did his best to ease his father into a comfortable position, but it was no use. No matter what way his father lay, he couldn't get any ease from the pain. "Da, I'll have to get ye home. Ye can't lie here," said Jake.

"Come on. I'll help ye to yer feet. Me ma'll know what to do."

His father grimaced with the pain. "I'm ... sorry ... Jake," he grunted.

"Come on, grab me shoulder," said Jake. "I'll pull ye to yer feet. Come on. Ye can't lie here." With a great effort, Jake hauled his father to his feet, but it was an exhausting and painful hour before they reached the cottage.

"Holy Mother of God!" exclaimed Mary when they came stumbling through the door. "What happened?"

Jake eased his father onto a stool near the fire.

"Jake," grunted his father." Would ye fill the basket? I'll need plenty of heat on me back. Then ye can help yer mother get me to bed."

Jake shook turf dust and small pieces of turf from the basket into the fire and then hurried to the door. Just as he stepped around the corner of the door, he heard his father cry out, "Mary, what are we goin' to do? Me back's finished. I know it is."

"We can get Willie Moran. He can rub in sinews and fix ye. He fixed John Thompson's bad ankle ..."

"No. We need no-one."

Mary sighed. She hated Paddy when he was stubborn, yet she couldn't say. "Jake should be able to keep goin' 'til ..."

"He's too young. The work would be too much fer him," said Paddy. "McConnell will find out soon enough. Ohhhh, damn!" he cried, almost falling off the stool.

As Jake filled the basket, he thought about their predicament. For a second or two he was angry with Eamon for emigrating, but now he worried. His father would need to rest for at least a week, maybe more. It was up to him now. He would have to do the work until his father got better.

***

But over the next four days his father's back didn't improve. Late the following night, McConnell and Samuel called. Without knocking, they barged into the cottage. Jake was sitting by the fire, repairing his threadbare trousers that had been torn in two places when he'd been mending a fence in the lower fields. He

27

was exhausted. McConnell studied Jake's father who lay on straw-filled bags near the fire. "I haven't seen ye at work recently, Miller," he said.

When Jake noticed Samuel looking around the cottage, he thought, what do they want?

"I hurt me back, sir," said Jake's father. "The night we were fixin' the cart. It's much better now." Grunting, he struggled to sit up, but he couldn't hide the pain from McConnell.

McConnell glanced at his son, then turned to Jake's father. "I suppose I'd better tell ye now, Miller," he said. "Samuel here is gettin' married." His son gaped at him. "He's goin' to need the cottage," continued the farmer.

"The cottage?" exclaimed Paddy, frowning. "What do ye mean, sir?" He looked at Mary. The shock showed on her face.

"What I mean is, I need the cottage fer me son and his wife," explained the farmer. He glanced around the cottage. "Yees have 'til the weekend to get out." He turned to go.

Jake's eyes were wide with the terrible realisation of what the farmer had said. McConnell was throwing them out of their home. He looked at Samuel. The farmer's son smirked at him.

"But, sir," cried Paddy. "We've got no place to go."

McConnell turned to Paddy, contempt showing on his face. "Ye should have thought on that when ye allowed yer son to emigrate. The farm has suffered this past year and it's all because yer not up to the work. Well, I don't need yees any more now." He glared at Jake and his parents. "I want yees all out of here by the weekend." Then, without another word, he strode out of the door into the darkness. Chuckling, Samuel strutted out after him.

Outside, Jake and his parents heard McConnell say something about marriage and Samuel laugh. Jake's face flushed with anger and, just then, he heard his father cry, "Mary, what are we goin' to do? Oh, God, what are we goin' to do now?"

"There's nothin' we can do, Paddy. I knew it would come to this. Yer back will never be strong enough fer the work, and McConnell knows it."

"But ... but he said he wants the cottage fer his son. He's gettin' married," said Paddy.

"His son's not gettin' married," exclaimed Mary. "Did ye not see his face? He was surprised when his father said it. Paddy," she cried, "don't ye understand? They're throwin' us out. They're evictin' us from our home."

Jake's eyes filled with tears, but suddenly he was running outside and up the lane. He caught up with McConnell and his son climbing into the cart. "Ye can't throw us out!" he cried, grabbing the cartwheel with both hands and holding on tightly. "Ye can't!"

"Oh, can't I?" shouted McConnell. "Lissen, ye scut ye. I can do anythin' I want with me own property."

"But I can do the work," pleaded Jake. "Please give me a chance. Don't throw us out. We have nowhere to go. I'll do the work. I'll do twice as much. Please ..."

"You," sneered Samuel. "Ye wee scut ye. How could ye do the work? How could ye tend the animals or drive a plough?"

"I could. I could. Please," pleaded Jake, gripping the wheel harder when McConnell lifted his whip to drive off. "Please, just give me a chance. Me da will be better soon. I can do the work 'til he is. Give me a chance ..."

"Outta me way!" shouted McConnell, whipping at the horse. The wheel spun, but Jake still held on. Suddenly, McConnell lashed at him. With a cry as the leather thong tore open his cheek, Jake let go and staggered back, holding his face. As he lay in the mud, blood seeping between his fingers, the cart trundled away. "I want yees all out by the weekend!" shouted McConnell.

The tears stung the cut on Jake's face as he cried out to God to help them.

EVICTED

They had received three letters from Eamon in the last year and that night, as he tried to sleep, Jake thought about his brother and how he was getting on. Jake had been sent with the letters to Bridget's house to get her to read them to him, as none of the Millers could read or write.

The first letter had told them that Eamon and Ann had a son, Patrick. Eamon also told them that he had a good job on a big farm outside Philadelphia. When Jake told his parents the news, the only comment from his father was, "Patrick could have been born here. Now we'll never see our only grandchild." Jake's mother had kissed the letter, and placed it in the niche at the bottom of the chimney breast, in the secret place where they kept their meagre savings.

The second letter brought the happy news that Ann was expecting again.

Some months later they had received a third letter telling them that Eamon and Ann were buying a house. The letter also informed them that Eamon had been promoted to foreman. Eamon said there was plenty of work on the farm and he could get jobs for all of them. He said he missed them and if they wished, he could get enough money to send them the fare to bring them over.

When Bridget had read this part of the letter to Jake, his heart had pounded with excitement. But when he told his father what Eamon had said, his father had snapped, "I'll never set a foot in that cursed place." Jake had looked at his mother, hoping she would try to persuade his father, but she just sighed quietly and said nothing.

***

It was a cold, frosty Saturday night when McConnell and his son came. Over those few days, and all that Saturday, Jake hoped McConnell had changed his mind. He had been out mending the fences and getting the pens ready, working late every night, hoping McConnell would realise that he could do the work.

Jake was exhausted and cold that night, and when he got home, his mother was massaging his father's back, which had improved slightly.

"Yer dinner's ready, Jake," said his mother. "I'll just finish yer father's back, then I'll serve it."

"I'll do it, ma," said Jake. He was about to lay out the bowls and spoons when the cottage door burst open. Jake was the nearest to it when the farmer and his son barged in.

"I thought I told yees I wanted yees out by the weekend!" shouted McConnell. Samuel smirked at Jake.

"But we've got no place to go," exclaimed Jake's father, pulling himself to his knees.

"Ye should have thought on that when ye allowed yer son to emigrate. He would have been able to do the work now yer not fit to."

"Sir, I can do the work. I've been doin' the work," said Jake. "Me da will be better in a week or so. I can ..."

"A week or so," sneered McConnell's son.

At that moment, Jake, who was not a violent boy, never felt more like hitting anyone as he did Samuel.

"Right!" shouted the farmer, kicking over a stool. "Out! Out!"

The horror of what was going to happen hit Jake all of a sudden. "Oh, please," cried his mother.

With a snarl, the farmer reached for her and began to drag her towards the door. As his father struggled to get to his feet to help her, Jake's temper broke. With a cry, he leapt at the farmer and began punching at the burly man's stomach. But Samuel grabbed the fallen stool and with a curse, swung it at Jake. It glanced off his shoulder and, with a grunt, he was sent spinning against the doorjamb. Dazed, he heard his father shout, "Please don't hurt Mary. We'll go! Please. Just don't hurt her!"

Jake, still dazed, felt himself being dragged through the door by McConnell's son. Unaware of the rain lashing against his face and the blood pouring from the laceration on his cheek, which had opened up again, Jake felt Samuel's boot thud into his ribs and, with a moan, he passed out.

***

When Jake regained consciousness, he stared up at the worried faces of his mother and father.

"Jake, are ye all right?" whispered his mother.

Remembering what had happened, Jake sat up. "Ow!" he groaned, feeling his bruised ribs. He looked around. They were sitting in the rain, just outside the gate, and all of them were soaked to the skin. Jake looked back at the cottage. The double doors were closed, and in the lamplight he could see the shadowy figures of McConnell and his son.

"Jake," grunted his father. "Are ye all right? Do ye think yer strong enough to help me to me feet? We can't stay here all night. We'll get our deaths out in this rain."

Groaning, Jake pulled himself to his feet and with the help of his mother, managed to get his father into an upright position.

"There's the overhang where the cattle shelter in the back fields," groaned his father. "We'll have to go there."

Jake frowned and looked at the cottage. "Maybe McConnell will let us stay the night," he said. He turned to his mother, but she shook her head.

They reached the overhang thirty-five minutes later and by then, rain was dripping from them like dozens of leaking water taps. The overhang was a place by the high ditch at the bottom of the field. Thick whin bushes grew over the ditch and down, almost touching the field. Under the bushes, the ground was dry and hard, and Jake and his mother eased Paddy down against the back of the overhang where it was driest. Before long, the three Millers were huddling close to each other for heat, still unable to comprehend what had happened. They sat listening to the rain lashing against the whins above them. Though it was dry, a few persistent drops struggled through the thick bushes to reach into their shelter. Suddenly, lightning flashed. The crash of thunder made them feel even more helpless and vulnerable.

A few minutes later, Mary gave a sudden cry. "Oh, Mother of God! I fergot."

"Ma," whispered Jake, startled. "What? What did ye ferget?"

"Our savin's," cried his mother. "And Eamon's letters. His address is on the back of the last one. No ... no ..." They looked at Jake's father. But he seemed not to have heard. He was staring, as if in a trance, up at the roof of the overhang.

Jake's breaths came in gasps. He had never felt so helpless. What were they going to do? he wondered. They had no clothes, only the rags they wore, and no money, nowhere to live.

A half-hour later, the rain stopped. It was then Jake noticed his mother shivering. "Ma," he whispered, glancing at his father. "Are ye all right?"

His mother gave him an encouraging smile. "Just a wee bit cold," she whispered. "But I'll be all right. Don't worry." Her smile didn't linger long and she pressed closer to Paddy for heat.

Jake studied his father. He seemed to be hardly breathing. "Ma," he whispered, "is me da all right?"

"Shhhh," hissed his mother, "he's just a bit shocked. He'll be all right. Let him rest."

Jake made up his mind then. "Ma," he whispered, "I'm goin' back to the cottage."

His mother gasped. "No, Jake. No. McConnell and his son will give ye another beating, maybe worse."

Jake gritted his teeth. "Ma, we need our savin's to survive. If we don't get them, we'll starve. I'm goin'."

"Jake, no," cried his mother. "Please ..."

Jake noticed his father hadn't overheard their conversation. "I'll be all right, ma," he whispered, sliding towards the entrance.

"Jake!" cried his mother.

But he was gone.

A Rescue and a Robbery

Stumbling through the darkness across several muddy fields and slipping along narrow lanes, Jake soon reached the cottage. As he approached it he could see light coming from inside. He also noticed that McConnell's cart and horse were gone. Guessing that McConnell or his son were inside, he slipped to the side window. He almost gasped aloud at what he saw.

Samuel was sitting at the table, eating Jake's dinner. But it was the money and Eamon's letters that had Jake's heart pounding. McConnell's son had discovered them and they were sitting in front of him on the table.

Suddenly, a fierce determination to get them back overcame Jake, and he knew he would have to face the farmer's son.

He groaned as he turned to look for something to use as a weapon. His ribs still ached. Quickly, he slipped around to the back of the cottage where he knew the broken shaft of a spade lay and, searching in the grass in the dim light, he soon found it. He was surprised at how light the shaft was. The jagged edge, where it had broken off, had a hole where the rusting rivet had held it to the blade. With his heart pounding harder than before, he made his way back to the door of the cottage. Gripping the jagged end of the shaft tightly, he took two deep breaths, then banged on the door. He was shocked when it swung open.

Startled and frightened, McConnell's son, still seated at the table, gaped at him, for Jake looked like some demon of the night. He was soaking wet and covered in mud. Blood was congealed on his pale face and his hair was hanging around his wild, staring eyes. Keeping the broken shaft hidden behind his back, Jake shouted, "I've come fer our savin's!"

Samuel's fear instantly vanished when he recognised who it was. He glanced at the money lying on the table. Nobody was going to take it from him. He had found it. His father didn't know about it and he never would. It was his. Scowling, he slowly stood up. As he did, Jake gulped. McConnell's son seemed to have grown bigger.

"And do you think I'm goin' to give it to ye?" snarled Samuel. "Just like that?" He gave a start when Jake brandished his makeshift weapon.

"It belongs to us!" shouted Jake. Then, before he realised what he was doing, he took two steps towards McConnell's son.

But with a curse, Samuel grabbed the stool he had been sitting on and with a scowl on his face, he held the stool in one hand. "Well then, come and get it!" he shouted.

Jake gulped again, but he was determined to get the money. Without it, they hadn't a hope of surviving.

It was Samuel who acted first and with a curse, he swung the stool at Jake. The stool hissed past Jake's head, just kissing his hair as he ducked in time. Quick as he could, though a little off balance, Jake whacked Samuel in the stomach. Then, before he knew what he was doing and as Samuel doubled over, he swung the shaft again, hitting him on the back of the neck. With a grunt, Samuel fell to the floor. Immediately, Jake darted to the table, scooped up the money and his brother's letters, then turned to head for the door. As he was about to step past Samuel, the farmer's son grabbed his ankle and he almost fell. But, kicking with his other foot, Jake was free, and all of a sudden he was through the door and racing into the darkness. Behind, he heard Samuel shout, "I'll get ye fer this, Miller!"

Gasping for breath, Jake ran on. As he did, the realisation of what he had done made him stop and vomit by the side of a ditch.

Seconds later he was hurrying back to the overhang. He reached it just as the rain began to fall again. "I got them, ma," he whispered, handing the money and Eamon's letters to her. He glanced at his father. He was asleep.

"Was there anyone about?" asked his mother.

"No," lied Jake. It was the first time he had ever lied to his mother.

The rain grew heavier, and somehow the noise as it battered the whins helped the exhausted boy to drift to sleep.

Daylight streaming into the overhang woke him and Jake gave a start when he remembered where he was.

"Are ye all right, Jake?" whispered his mother.

"Aye, but I'm starvin', ma," said Jake, sitting up. He looked at his father. He was still asleep. "What are we goin' to do, ma?" he asked. "We can't stay here. We'll st ..." He was going to say starve to death, but he stopped.

"We'll have to make fer Derry," said his mother. "We'll surely get help there." She looked at Paddy. He was muttering to himself. "We'll let yer father sleep a while longer, then we'll see how he is when he wakes."

When Jake's father woke, he seemed a little stronger, and minutes later they had reached the rocky main road to Derry. They were a sorry sight, with Jake's father supported between them and mud and blood caked on Jake's face, hair and clothes. His mother's skirt was covered in mud. All three Millers were soaked, cold and hungry.

It was several minutes before Jake realised that at the pace they were walking they would not reach Derry until late in the day. They were growing weaker all the time. He knew they needed food.

An hour later, with the rain just a light mizzle, they heard the sound of a cart and horse on the road behind them. Frightened that it might be McConnell or his son, Jake told his mother to help him get his father over to the side of the road by some bushes. As they hid there, Jake peered through the bushes and saw it was a farmer carrying vegetables to market. When the cart drew near, Jake saw two thin, scruffy-looking men sitting in the back with the vegetables. Quickly, he made up his mind. "Ma, hold me da."

Jake suddenly stepped into the middle of the muddy road as the cart came up to them.

"Whoa! Whoa there!" screamed the young man driving the cart. He wore a long black coat and cap. He glared at Jake as he pulled the horse and cart to a halt.

"I'm sorry if I startled ye, sir, but I saw ye were goin' to the market, and I was wonderin' if ye would sell me some carrots and a turnip," said Jake.

The young farmer took in Jake's appearance. "Have ye any money?" he asked.

"I can pay," said Jake. He looked into the cart. There were about a hundred turnips, bunches of carrots and several bags of potatoes. "How much fer, say, ten carrots and a turnip?" Jake reckoned that would keep them going until they reached Derry.

The young man counted. "Turnips, a penny. Carrots, a dozen, say tuppence. Thruppence all together."

"Hold on and I'll get the money," said Jake. He hurried across to his mother and father. "Ma," he whispered. "I need thruppence. I'm buying some carrots and a turnip. That should feed us 'til we get to Derry."

Aware that the three men were watching, Jake's mother turned her back to them and a few seconds later she handed Jake the money. The jingle of coins as she put the bag into her pocket had one of the two men in the back of the cart nudging the other.

Jake returned to the farmer and held up the money. The young man reached for it. "Carrots and the turnip first," said Jake.

Turning to one of the men in the back of the cart, the farmer said, "Throw him out a big turnip and a bunch of those carrots." When the deal was done, the farmer smiled. "Nice to have done business with ye. Are yees goin' to Derry?"

Jake nodded.

"I'd give yees a lift but I've no room. Picked up these two a while back. Anyway, I must get on. Thanks." He cracked his whip at his scrawny-looking horse and as the cart drove away, Jake saw the men in the back looking at his mother. One of them whispered something to the other. Seconds later the cart was out of sight.

As Jake and his parents sat eating by the roadside, his father sighed. "At least we have food and we're together."

"Paddy," said Mary. "When we get to Derry we'll have to get word sent to Eamon somehow. We'll see Bridget ..."

Jake looked hopefully at his father.

"Never!" shouted Paddy, bits of carrot spitting from his mouth. "I'll never ask him fer help." He glared at Mary. "And if yees," he looked at Jake, "any of yees, send to him fer help,

I'll ... I'll ... I'd rather die than ask him fer help. Ye hear me? I'd rather die."

"Ach, Paddy," exclaimed his wife. "You and yer pride."

"I mean it, Mary. He's not to know what we've come to. We've enough ... money?" He frowned. "Where did ye get the money to buy the vegetables?" he asked her.

"I went back to the cottage when ye were sleepin', da," said Jake. "I got the savin's."

His father stared at him. "Was McConnell there?" Jake shook his head. His father sighed. "Thank God fer that." He turned to Mary. "How much have we, Mary?"

"Two pounds, three shillin's and tuppence," said Jake's mother.

"Enough to feed us 'til I can get work," said Paddy, smiling.

Jake looked at his mother. They both knew his father would never be fit for hard work again.

"Come on," said Paddy, "let's get goin'. The sooner we can get to Derry, the sooner I can get work." Groaning loudly, he straightened. Jake helped his mother stuff the rest of the vegetables into her wet shawl. As they headed back on the road to Derry, Jake could see his father was in better spirits. His father really believed he would get work, and neither he nor his mother was going to put him off his notion.

***

Ten minutes later, they were passing a long line of oak trees at a bend in the road when suddenly, a voice from the trees shouted, "Give us yer money and ye'll not be harmed!"

Terrified, they saw two men step from the trees. It was the men who had been in the back of the farmer's cart.

"We ... we've no money," said Jake's father.

The taller of the men, who carried a stout wooden cudgel, scowled. "I said hand over yer money and ye'll not be harmed."

"I told ye," exclaimed Jake's father. "We've got no money. Does it luk as if we would have money?"

Jake studied the robbers. He knew that if his father had been at his full strength they might have had a chance against the robbers, but with his father's back the way it was, they didn't. He looked at his mother. She realised that if the robbers did attack them, Jake or her husband would be injured. "We need the money," she cried. "We've been thrown out of our home. We need what little we have to feed us."

Jake's father glared at her. Now the robbers knew they had money. "Yer not gettin' it," he said, trying to straighten, but grimacing with pain, he almost fell.

Suddenly one of the men grabbed at Jake's mother. Jake immediately leapt to defend her, but the man with the cudgel struck him on the side of the head, and with stars exploding around him, Jake fell unconscious to the muddy ground.

BEGGING IN DERRY

Their voices seemed far away and Jake could hear his mother crying. "Paddy, we'll have to get help! We can't just lie here. Jake's been hurt. Paddy, fer God's sake!"

"Mary, what can I do?" Now Jake heard his father start to cry. Their voices faded.

***

When Jake regained consciousness, his head was throbbing. It was dark. Rain spat into his face and he licked at the water. Groaning, he tried to sit upright. The pain grew worse, thudding like a Lambeg drum, each thud feeling like it would burst his head open.

"Lie still, Jake," whispered his mother. Gently, she dabbed at the congealed blood caked on the cut at the side of his head.

Jake looked all around. They were lying at the foot of a high wall. "Whe ... where are we?" he gasped. His mouth was dry. He licked again at the rain running down his face.

"Derry," said his father. "Beneath the Siege Walls." He looked anxiously at him. "Are ye all right, son? How's yer head? Ye got a wile crack on it."

"Our savin's!" exclaimed Jake, suddenly remembering the robbers.

"Stolen," whispered his mother.

"How did ... owwww." Jake blinked back tears of pain.

"Here, lie back, son," whispered Paddy, reaching to ease Jake against the cold stone wall.

"But how did we get here?" asked Jake when the nauseating dizziness had subsided a little.

"Another farmer came along," answered his father. "He took pity on us and gave us a lift to the market. We carried ye here."

"Ye carried me? But yer back ..."

His father smiled grimly. "I'll have to get used to the pain. It doesn't luk like me back will ever be as good again."

Jake frowned. "It'll get better, da," he whispered. "And when I'm strong enough, I'll get a job. I'll luk after ye. Both of yees."

At this, Mary gave a little cry and turned away. When she turned back, Jake saw tears in her eyes. Suddenly she rose to her feet. "I'll have to be goin' now, Paddy," she said, looking at her surprised son.

"Goin'?" Jake frowned. "Where?"

"I won't be long. Keep an eye on Jake's head. If it bleeds again, use this to clean it," said Mary, handing Paddy a piece of wet rag. Then, wrapping her wet shawl around her narrow shoulders, and with a glance at Jake, she disappeared into the darkness.

"Ma!" Jake cried after her. "Owww." He held his head as he turned to his father. "Da, where's she goin'?" he gasped. His father turned away and it was then Jake realised he was crying. "Da?"

His father's words shocked him. "She's gone to the streets to beg," he croaked. "Jake, we need money fer food."

"Beg? But, da ..."

"I know," exclaimed his father. "I know. Ye don't have to say it."

Jake pulled himself up. His head felt as if it were about to explode and he felt sick. "Da," he said quietly. "I can beg. Me ma doesn't have to."

With tears running down his face, his father suddenly hugged him, crying, "I know, son. I know." Gently he eased away from him. "Let's see if ye feel any better when yer mother gets back, eh?" he whispered.

As they lay shivering, Jake silently cursed the rain. It always seems to be raining, he thought.

Mary returned two hours later. All the time she had been away, Jake and his father had worried. With a heavy sigh, she dropped between them, cuddling close to her husband for heat. Jake and Paddy pressed closer to her. "Nothin'," she croaked. "Not a farthin'. Paddy, ye wouldn't believe the many that are beggin' in the streets. I've never thought about the poor in Derry before, but there are others as bad off as we are, some worse."

"What could be worse than this?" sighed her husband.

"We could be crippled, or diseased, or a lot worse," snapped Mary. "We could have lost our son today." She examined Jake's head. "Paddy, luk, we'll have to get word to our Eamon ..."

"No!" His father's shout numbed Jake's head and he groaned. "I'd rather starve to death than ask him fer help!" shouted Jake's father. "Do ye hear me? I'd rather starve!"

"Aye, well, that's what's goin' to happen to us!" screamed Jake's mother. She sniffed back a tear as she glanced at Jake. "Paddy, what are we goin' to do? Tell me! Tell me! Tell me ..." She began to cry. Paddy stared at Jake as he reached to hold Mary close.

The rain grew heavier and the biting wind began to gust around the unfortunate Millers as they huddled for warmth at the foot of the damp Derry Walls.

As they lay shivering, trying to sleep, Jake recalled his father's words to his brother. *"If ye go, then what's left fer us? The Workhouse, that's what, the curse of the poor, the Derry Workhouse."* Oh, Eamon, thought Jake. Why did ye have to go? Why did ye have to leave us?

***

They woke early next morning, cold and hungry. Jake's head felt a lot better, but was very painful to touch. As they ate the rest of the carrots and pieces of turnip, they discussed what they were going to do. Jake had suggested they should try to contact one of Eamon's friends, either Thomas or James, but his father wouldn't hear of it.

It was a mizzling, grey day when they headed through Magazine Gate and over towards Shipquay Street. The cobbled streets glistened with rain. In the 1870s, Derry was a bustling city. People hurried everywhere, most of them women on their way to the shirt factories, shirt making being Derry's main industry. Some of the women stared at Jake and his parents. Others hurried past.

"Can ye help us, please?" Jake's mother asked, holding out her hand to a woman who was hurrying past. "Money fer somethin' to eat. Please." The woman narrowed her eyes at her and, without a word, hurried on.

Jake's face flushed with anger. This was all Eamon's fault. His mother was begging in the street. They were beggars. Then a man wearing a black coat was about to walk past them. Before he realised what he was doing, Jake said, "Please, sir, can ye help us?" He held out his hand as he stepped in front of the man, blocking his way.

"Out of my way, gypsy!" the man roared, pushing Jake away. Immediately, Jake was spun against an iron railing outside a house on the corner of the street. As his head glanced off the railing, he slid with a groan to the ground.

"Jake," cried his mother, going to him, "are ye all right?" His father scowled after the man.

"I'm ... I'm all right, ma," grunted Jake as he struggled to his feet. But blood was trickling down the side of his head and along his neck. He swayed and though still dizzy, he saw another man approaching. "Sir," he gasped, pushing towards him, "could ye let us have somethin' to buy food, sir? Please, sir." He held out his grubby hand.

The man frowned, gaped at the blood on Jake's face and then studied Jake's mother and father. Quickly, he searched in his pocket, and Jake's eyes widened as the man handed him a farthing. "Thank ye, sir," he muttered.

"God bless ye, sir," called his mother as the man hurried on.

Jake smiled at her. It was a beginning. Suddenly he felt faint and, with a sigh, he slid to the ground.

"Jake!" His mother bent to him, and glancing at Paddy, she said, "Jake, luk, just you lie there." Gently, she began to clean the blood from his pale face. "Lie there and don't move. Yer hurt. Yer father and me are goin' to see if we can get some food."

"But, ma ... I can help ..." began Jake.

"No, son," said his father. "Yer too weak. Rest. When we get enough money, we'll try and find better shelter." But towards the end of the day, as darkness and more rain came, they had only managed to beg three farthings and a halfpenny.

They returned to the foot of the Walls where they ate nearly all of a stale loaf of bread and drank two thirds of a quart of buttermilk that they had bought with the money. The food seemed to help Jake, though the throbbing in his head was still there.

Later, Mary got ready to go out begging again. This time Jake was determined to go with her.

They returned late that night without being able to beg anything.

***

It began to snow early in the morning and when they woke, frozen to the bone, an inch of snow lay all around them. Jake's head was a lot better, though he felt too cold to notice. Mary examined it. "The blood has caked all around it," she said. "It seems to be all right. At least there's no infection." She smiled at him.

Shivering, they finished off the bread and the rest of the cold buttermilk. As they got ready to go into the streets to beg again, they heard a chapel bell ring. "My God, it's Sunday!" exclaimed Jake's mother.

"Ma," said Jake, an idea coming to him. "Why can't we go to the chapel? We could ask the priest fer help. Surely ..."

His mother shook her head. "That first night I was out beggin', I met several people worse than us, sick people. They told me there wasn't any help from anyone. The priests hardly have enough fer themselves. They used to help, but there was so many needed it they had to stop." She frowned as she listened to the pealing of the distant chapel bells in the clear, frosty air. "We'd need to go to Mass. Aye," she said, shivering as she got to her feet. "We'll go to Mass."

Jake and Paddy stared at her, but seconds later Jake was helping his father to his feet and before long, they were making their way through the streets towards the Long Tower Chapel. People heading for Mass stared at them. Some blessed themselves, glad they were not in the situation the unfortunate Millers had found themselves.

Inside, the chapel felt colder. They had only sat down when the priest came out to the altar. As they prayed, shivering with the rest of the congregation, Jake thought about Sundays at home. They had always walked to chapel in the Waterside part of Derry every Sunday, no matter what the weather was like. Jake had always enjoyed the ceremony and meeting other people. But now he couldn't pray. God had let them down. What sort of a God, he thought, would allow them to end up like this?

When the Gospel finished, the priest began his sermon. "On this day, the eighth of December ..."

Suddenly, Mary gave a little cry and stood up. "The eighth of December," she cried. Everyone stared at her. The priest coughed and nodded for her to sit down.

"Sit down," a stout woman behind Jake hissed.

All of a sudden, Mary ran crying from the chapel. Frowning, Jake and Paddy quickly followed her outside. They found her crying near the tiny grotto by the side of the chapel. "What is it, Mary?" asked Jake's father.

With tears in her eyes, Mary looked at Jake. "December the eighth," she cried. "It's yer birthday, Jake ... yer birthday." She began to cry louder.

Jake stared at her. He was twelve.

Thirteen Steps to Hell

"Ma, I don't mind about me birthday. Really ..." said Jake with tears in his own eyes.

"But *I* do, Jake. *I* do." cried his mother. "I was planning on a wee birthday party fer ye when ... when ..."

"Ma," whispered Jake, "I'll have other birthdays. Don't be upsettin' yersel'."

It took almost a half-hour before Jake and his father could pacify her. Some of the people had stared at them when they came out of Mass and Jake had taken the opportunity to beg from them. That was until a young priest came out and told them they would have to beg somewhere else.

By one o'clock they had begged two farthings. As they headed through Bishop's Gate towards Shipquay Street, they came to a small baker's shop. Though it was Sunday, it was open. Inside, the baker, a fat man with flour patches on his round face, frowned when he saw the Millers stop outside his shop window. Moments later, Jake and his mother entered the shop.

"Could ye sell us a fresh loaf, sir?" asked Mary. She licked her dry lips as she looked at a row of six freshly-baked, hot pan loaves sitting on the counter.

Suddenly, the baker gave a start and his eyes widened with horror. "Out!" he bellowed. Jake gaped at him. "Out! Out!" screamed the baker, and with a bellow, he rounded the counter, his rolling pin held aggressively above his head. His massive stomach jiggled beneath his flour-bag apron.

"But ... we've money ..." protested Mary, backing away. She was surprised by the baker's attitude.

"Ye've got lice, that's what ye have!" shouted the baker. "Out! I don't want them crawlin' all over my shop. Out!"

"Lice," muttered Mary as she quickly left the shop with Jake.

"And don't come back!" shouted the baker, his face almost as red as the jam in one of his buns.

Outside, Mary examined Jake's head. She had noticed him scratching it earlier, but she had thought it was because of his injury and she knew it would get itchy when it began to heal. But now, horrified, she drew back. With a cry, she swung to examine Paddy's head. "Paddy," she cried. "We've got lice ... and probably fleas." Almost screaming, she rubbed at her head. "We've got lice ... ahhhh!" Suddenly she reached for Jake and began to run her fingers hard through his thick hair. One of her fingers caught on the cut in his head and with a yell, he pulled away.

"Ma!"

All of a sudden, Mary fell to her knees, crying. Jake and his father stared at her. Jake's mother had always been over-fussy about cleanliness and it had sometimes irritated him. He scratched at the back of his neck and up into his hair. Lice, he thought, shuddering.

They begged the rest of that day, trying to ignore the terrible itching, and at around seven o'clock they had only managed to get a farthing from an old woman who had taken pity on them. The shops were closed by then and they were unable to buy any food.

Later, when it was dark, they made their way down Carlisle Road, and in a gateway near the bottom, they sheltered from the icy wind that blasted up the road. As they huddled there, ravenous and scratching, Mary whispered, "Paddy, we have to get help. We can't live like this."

Jake squinted in the darkness, trying to see his father's face. It was covered in grey-white hair and he was scratching at it. "Mary," his father whispered. "Ye know there's only one place we'll get help." He glanced at Jake.

"Then we'll have to go there," said Mary. "Paddy, we'll just have to."

Jake frowned as he scratched furiously at the top of his head. There was somewhere they could go for help? he thought. Why haven't we gone there long ago? "Where are ye talkin' about, ma?" he asked. His father looked away.

"On the other side of the bridge," said Mary, turning to Paddy. "Paddy," she whispered, nodding for him to tell Jake.

Paddy gave a huge sigh. "She's talkin' about ... about the Workhouse, Jake," he said, his voice almost breaking.

Jake's heart pounded with fear as the dreaded word sank in. "But, da ..." he began.

"We have to go there, Jake," said his mother. "There's no-one else will help us, except ..."

"No!" snapped Paddy. "No. And anyway, it's too late fer that."

The Workhouse, thought Jake, trembling.

But suddenly, crying, Mary rose to her feet. "We're not sleepin' out in this weather another night. Paddy, we need to get washed. We need someone to luk after us. We need to go now. I can't stand this any longer. No-one cares whether we live or die. At least in the Workhouse we'll have a roof over our heads, and food to eat, a place to wash ourselves ..."

"Mary, if we go there we're finished," said Jake's father.

"Oh, Paddy," cried Mary, "We're finished anyway. We're infested. We're filthy. Filthy and stinkin'! Filthy and ..." She began to cry louder.

Paddy rose slowly to his feet and reached to hug her to him. All of a sudden, Jake was also on his feet and all three were hugging and crying as the lice jumped from one head to the other and burrowed deep.

They were almost halfway across Carlisle Bridge ten minutes later, heading towards the Waterside area. The wind whistled through their threadbare clothes, chilling them, and as it did, Jake looked down at the dark, fast river that had taken his brother away. Suddenly he stopped and spat venomously through the wooden rails at the water. His mother, stopping too, reached out, gripped his hand, and gave him an encouraging smile.

Soon, they were heading down Duke Street towards Glendermott Road. A few minutes later they were approaching a wide bend in the road; and there it was.

The moon lit up the dreaded two-storey Derry Workhouse that stood on an elevated site. In front of it was an iron gate with a row of concrete steps leading up to a path to the front door. As they stumbled up the slippery steps, their dread increasing with each second, Jake was unconsciously counting the steps. Thirteen, he thought, when he reached the top; thirteen steps to hell.

His legs felt as if they would buckle under his body as he followed his parents along the path to the black oak door. There, his father turned to look at them. Tears were running down his pale, gaunt face. Mary sniffed and nodded for him to knock. Paddy wiped his face with his sleeve, then turned and reached for the heavy knocker and rapped twice. The hollow sound echoed from inside as he stepped back to stand beside Jake and Mary. They waited for a minute.

"Maybe there's no-one in," said Jake hopefully.

His father knocked again. Three times. The echoes had hardly died away when the door creaked open. A tall, red-haired man glared at them. "Well," he snapped, looking with contempt at the unfortunate Millers.

"We ..." began Paddy, glancing at Jake and Mary. "We need help."

"Help? Hah!" said the man, who was the porter. He held the door wider as he studied them, but then, with a disgusted sigh, he said, "Follow me to the probation room. And close that god-fersaken door after yees. That wind out there would skin ye the night."

Jake trembled as he followed his mother inside. Paddy closed the door behind them. They were inside the Derry Workhouse. Jake could almost feel the horror of the place like a great weight forcing his head lower. A dull light ahead showed them the dark silhouette of the porter and they followed him along the hall until, shortly, they were shown into a small room with a low wooden bench along the far wall.

"Wait there," said the porter. "I'll see if the Master will receive yees." He disappeared into the darkness.

Jake and his parents looked around the room. In the dull light, they could see rough stone walls that had been white-washed many times. The ceiling was of bare rafters and the floor of cold mortar. Huddling together, the Millers waited on the bench. They couldn't bear to look at each other. Paddy stared dejectedly at the floor. Mary had an arm linked through his as she stared at the open door. Jake's thoughts were on his brother. He wished he were in America with him. He wondered how Eamon was doing.

Almost a half-hour later, the porter returned. "The Master will see yees now. I'll warn yees, he's not in the best of moods. Only speak when yer spoken to and keep well back from his desk. I've told him yer dirty ..."

"Dirty?" Paddy looked at Mary.

They followed the porter along a narrow passage and into the receiving room which was not much bigger than the probation room. The only furniture in the room was a low desk and chair. The only light was from a small oil lamp, which sat on the right of the top of the desk. The dull light threw dark shadows on the walls as the flame flickered occasionally in the draughty room. The walls were ghostly white and the ceiling of strapped, plastered wood. The floor was cold and covered in concrete slabs.

The porter herded the Millers into a position about three yards from the desk. Sitting there was a thin man, his stern face just visible from the light of the oil lamp. He was writing in a thick book. On the other side of the book was a crockery inkpot. The Master glanced up for a second as he dipped his quill pen into it. He wore a black suit. He had a sharp, long nose, a pockmarked face and beady crafty eyes.

"Stay there and don't move," whispered the porter. "Don't go any nearer to the Master." With that, he turned and left the room. The Millers hardly heard the door close after him.

Shivering, they studied the Master. His very appearance filled them with dread. They knew they could expect very little help from him. As for Jake, he knew he was looking at the devil. No-one could look so evil. He studied the Master's hands. They were bony, skeletal. Jake had seen a human skeleton once when they had been digging down along the river. The body had been stripped clean by rats and other vermin and had been found lying tangled among the brown seaweed and glar.

After about three minutes, the Master looked at them. Before speaking, he studied each of the Millers in turn. Suddenly, "You!" he snapped, pointing to Paddy. His voice was harsh and resounded around the room in hollow waves of sound. "Name?"

Jake's father frowned. "Eh?"

"Yer name, man," snapped the Master. "If ye have one. What is it?"

"Oh," said Paddy. "Patrick. Patrick Miller."

The Master gave a start. He narrowed his eyes at him. "Patrick Miller what?" he snapped.

Paddy glanced at his wife. "Patrick Miller nothin'," he said to the Master.

The Master gritted his teeth. "Miller," he said, his lip curling. "When ye address yer betters, and that's me, ye'll address me as 'sir'. Do ye understand, Miller? Sir! Now, what is yer name?"

"Patrick Miller ... er ... sir," replied Paddy quickly.

The Master's jaw tightened and he began to write Paddy's name in the book. He stopped. "Is that Miller with an 'e', or Millar with an 'a'?"

"Eh? I'm sorry, sir. I don't know what ye mean," said Paddy.

The Master gave a long, exasperated sigh. "Is yer name spelt Mill-*e*-r, or Mill-*a*-r?"

"Oh," said Paddy, understanding now what the Master meant. "With an 'e'." The Master glared at him. "Sir," said Paddy quickly. "With an 'e', sir."

Jake was growing quickly angry at the degrading way they were being treated. Mary, feeling him tense, reached to hold his hand.

The Master, seeing her show of affection, studied Jake for a few seconds before writing and muttering, "Miller with an 'e'. Religion?"

"What?" asked Paddy. "Sir. What, sir?"

The Master threw his pen on the desk. "Miller with an 'e', are ye deaf? I asked ye what religion ye are. What church do ye attend? That's if ye attend any."

"The Waterside Chapel, sir," answered Paddy. "We're Catholics."

Writing it down, the Master said, "Roman Catholic. Age?"

"Forty-nine." The Master glared at him. "Er ... sir. Forty-nine, sir," said Paddy quickly.

The sound of the scratching of the Master's pen was making Jake's teeth ache.

"Forty-nine-year-old male," said the Master, writing. "Have ye any other family besides these two, any relatives?" he asked.

Paddy frowned. He glanced at Mary. "No, sir," he answered. "Only the three of us."

At this, Mary said, "We have a ..." Widening his eyes, Paddy pushed Mary to silence her.

The Master glared at Jake's mother. "Woman," he snapped, "ye'll speak when yer spoken to, and not before. Now tell me, what is yer name?"

"M ... Mary Miller, sir," whispered Mary, turning to stare at Paddy. He frowned and shook his head at her, warning her to say nothing about Eamon.

"What d'ye say?" said the Master. "Woman, ye'll have to speak louder."

"Mary Miller, sir," repeated Mary.

The Master spoke as he wrote, "Mary Miller with an 'e'. Religion?"

"Catholic, sir."

"Roman Catholic," said the Master, writing it down. "Age?"

"Forty-two, sir," said Mary, looking at Paddy again.

"Forty-two-year-old female," said the Master as he wrote it down. Now he looked at Jake. "You, boy," he said, dipping the quill deep into the inkpot.

"Jake Miller with an 'e'. I'm a Catholic and me age is elev ... twelve," said Jake sharply.

The Master glared at him, and Jake, unafraid, glared back. "Boy," snarled the Master, "yer insolence will soon be stamped out in here." He quickly wrote down Jake's name, religion and age. When he was finished, he pushed the book to the top of the desk and looked at Paddy. "Miller with an 'e'," he said, "what trade have ye?"

"Trade ... sir? I have none. I'm a farm worker, that's all," replied Paddy.

"Farm worker, eh? Good. We have need of someone with farm experience. We grow our own food here, food that will be consumed by yees and other Workhouse wastrels." He narrowed his eyes. "Now tell me, what circumstances brought ye to seek refuge in the Workhouse?"

"We were thrown out of the cottage we rented from McConnell, that's the farmer I worked fer," answered Paddy. "He said he needed it fer his son who was gettin' married. But he was tellin' lies. It was because I hurt me back and couldn't do the work. I've worked fer him since me wife and I got married. I've never missed a day and that's how I was rewarded, thrown out of our home."

The Master studied Paddy for a few seconds. "How's yer back now?" he asked.

"It ... it's much better, sir," said Paddy, straightening.

The Master narrowed his eyes as he studied Paddy another while. "What have ye been doin' since ye were thrown ... evicted from yer employer's property?"

"Nothin', sir. I could find no work. We slept in the fields the first night, then made our way to Derry. We were robbed of all our savin's on the way." Paddy bowed his head. "We've been beggin' ever since. But we couldn't get enough to feed us. There are so many beggin' in Derry these days ..."

"And so ye came here thinkin' ye'd be luked after and cared fer, did yees?" sneered the Master.

"We hoped ..." began Paddy.

"Hope! Hah! Miller, there's no hope in here. Maybe ye'd like to hear what it's like in the Workhouse. Maybe when ye find out what yer life here will be like, ye'll prefer beggin' in the streets." He glanced at Jake. "First of all, you and yer wife and yer offspring will be separated. Ye'll only see each other at prayers and mealtimes ..."

Jake gulped. Was it true? he thought. Was he to be separated from his mother and father?

The Master's voice droned on as he spat out the words. "Ye'll have three meals a day. Yer breakfast, which will be preceded by prayers and will be at six o'clock every mornin', will consist of seven ounces of oatmeal porridge and a half-quart of buttermilk. Fer yer dinner ye will get three-and-a-half pounds of potatoes and a quart of buttermilk. Supper will consist of five ounces of porridge and a half-quart of buttermilk." He smiled. "Ye'll learn to like stirabout."

His smile vanished as he continued. "Between meals, Miller, you will be either workin' in the gardens or breakin' stones with yer son. Yer back will soon get stronger and if it doesn't, ye'll be thrown out onto the street again. You, woman, will scrub the floors and furniture, sew and mend the Workhouse clothes, or work in the kitchen or laundry. Aye, the three of yees will be kept well occupied and yer life in the Workhouse will be made so miserable that yer only desire will be to leave it." He glared at them for several seconds and then suddenly stood up. "Now, get out of me sight!"

Paddy looked at Jake and Mary. "Sir ..."

"What?" snapped the Master.

"I was wonderin' if ye could see yer way to givin' us somethin' to eat now. We ..."

"What!" shouted the Master. "Get out! Porter! Porter!" Suddenly the door swung open with a crash and, with his face flushed, the porter rushed in. "Get these filthy wastrels out of me sight," screamed the Master. "Get them to the washrooms and have them deloused and scrubbed clean."

"Aye, sir," said the porter, pulling Paddy by the arm.

Jake glared at the Master and bunched his fists with anger. "Jake," whispered his mother, nodding for him to come with them. "Please ..."

With a glare at the Master, Jake allowed her to lead him from the receiving room.

THE BOYS' DORMITORY

Jake was taken to the washroom where his clothes were torn off him by Reggie, the porter's assistant. Reggie was a balding, surly young man with a huge red nose. The washroom had a mortar floor and was very cold. By a spotless, white delftware sink was a tub of cold water, and beside the tub was a slatted wooden chair.

Jake was pushed into the room and told by Reggie to wait, and now he stood shivering near the door. He gave a start when three scrawny boys came into the washroom. Frightened and embarrassed, he held his hands over his lower body to cover himself. The boys were thin, with pale, ghostly faces and hollow eyes. Suddenly Jake's nightmare came to him. He was living it. He was in the Workhouse. He studied the boys. Two were smaller than he was, and the boy holding a thick bar of carbolic soap was around Jake's size. Each boy wore a pair of grey trousers made of barragon that hung halfway down their legs. The boys wore shirts of grey Galway flannel. One of the smaller boys carried a pair of huge scissors; the other, a white delftware jug.

"I'll have to cut yer hair all off," said the boy with the scissors.

"What?" Jake gaped at him.

"The lice have to be cut out and yer head washed," said the thinnest of the boys who had black rings around his sunken dark eyes and who coughed occasionally.

"Naw," said Jake, stepping back. "Yer not gettin' near me with them scissors."

The boys looked at each other. Then the boy with the scissors took a step towards Jake, saying, "What's yer name?"

"Jake. Jake Miller."

"Jake," said the boy. "The lice have to be cut out and yer head washed. If it isn't, ye'll infect us all."

Jake frowned, but he stood his ground.

"Please," pleaded the boy with the jug. "The Master will have us locked in the Punishment Room if you don't."

"The what?" exclaimed Jake.

"The Punishment Room," said the boy with the scissors. "Luk, yer hair will soon grow back again. If I don't cut the lice away, the Master will have the porter and Reggie and some of the men do it. They'll hurt ye."

Removing one of his hands, Jake quickly scratched his head. The itching was worse.

"Jake, I won't hurt ye," said the boy with the scissors. "Honest. I'll leave as much of yer hair on as I can." He smiled.

Jake sighed. The itching was driving him to distraction. The loss of his hair would be a small price to pay to get rid of it. He nodded; then the boy reached out and Jake allowed him to lead him to the chair. The boy with the scissors moved behind him while the other boys knelt in front of Jake. One of them then dipped the bar of soap into the tub and began to soap Jake's feet and legs. The other boy, using a rag, washed the dirt from them. Jake's shoulders sagged when he saw his hair falling all around him and tears tumbled down his face as the shame of what was happening finally hit him. Ten minutes later, the irritating 'snip, snip' of the scissors stopped.

"There," said the boy who had cut his hair. "That's yer head clear of lice. Now, if ye'll step into the tub, we'll wash yer head and back."

Jake rose and, still holding his hands to cover himself, he stepped into the tub. The freezing water numbed him.

"Ye'll have to kneel down in it, Jake," said the boy with the soap.

Trembling from both the cold and shame, Jake knelt down. The boy then dipped the soap into the water and Jake gave a start when he slapped it onto his back and began to wash it. Using some of the suds, the boy who had cut his hair began to wash Jake's head. The carbolic stung the laceration, but the boy rubbed furiously at Jake's head, careful to avoid his injury. The third boy dipped the jug into the water, filled it, then poured it over Jake's head. Soap stung his eyes, but Jake hardly felt it.

"Ye'll have to wash down there yersel'," said the boy who had cut his hair, nodding to Jake's lower body. "We'll wait outside. I'll get ye a pair of trousers and a shirt. Give us a shout when yer done." With a quick glance at Jake, the boys left the washroom.

Jake stared at the door; suddenly it was all too much for him. He began to cry again. Hunched over the tub, he stared at the water. It was almost as dirty as the river that had carried his brother away. "Oh, God, Eamon," he cried. "Why did ye have to go? Why? Why?"

One of the boys stuck his head around the door a couple of minutes later. "Are ye done?" he asked. Jake nodded.

Two of the boys came in again. One carried clothes and the other a rough cloth. Handing the cloth to the shivering Jake, he said, "Here, dry yersel', then put on these clothes. They should fit ye."

They watched as Jake turned his back to them, stepped out of the tub and began to dry himself. When he was dressed he felt much better. A minute later, he followed the boys along a dark hall. The boy leading carried a small oil lamp. They climbed steep, broad stairs, holding onto a shaky white wooden banister. The hollow 'thud, thud' of their bare feet echoed around them until they came to an open door leading to the boys' dormitory.

Pale-faced boys stared at the new arrival as he came into the dormitory. The boys' dormitory resembled the inside of a ship with broad wooden beams and struts angling across the long, narrow room that was actually the attic of the Workhouse. A path in the centre of the dormitory was a yard wide and ran to a back wall of red brick. On each side of the path on raised platforms lay the boys' beds. These were simple canvas bags stuffed with straw.

Jake was shown to a bed near the back wall by the boy who had cut his hair. As he sat down, he became aware of a boy aged about eight who was crying. The boy was curled into a ball and had his back to Jake. Jake was just about to ask him what the matter was when, suddenly, one of the boys hissed, "It's Matron." Immediately, all the boys lay down. Jake, still sitting, stared down the dormitory as a tall woman carrying a small oil lamp came striding up.

The Matron was a stout woman in her mid-forties. She had tight, crafty eyes that darted here and there as she walked to the top of the dormitory. She wore a white apron, black-laced boots and an ankle-length brown dress. She stopped at Jake's bed. "Yer the new one," she said. "Miller?"

Jake nodded.

"Get up!" snapped the Matron.

Still weak, Jake struggled to get to his feet. "Hurry up! Hurry up!" snapped the Matron.

When Jake stood beside her, she said, "Turn around." Jake winced as the Matron held up the lamp with one hand and held tight to his left ear with the other. She peered into it, then snapped his head around and examined his other ear. "Ears clean," she muttered. "Show me yer mouth." Jake frowned.

Whack! The Matron's hard slap stunned him and he almost fell back as she shouted, "Are ye stupid, Miller! Yer not deaf! I asked ye to show me yer mouth. I won't ask again," she added coldly. Jake's face flushed with anger, but he thrust his head at the Matron and opened his mouth. She looked into it. "I'll expect ye to keep yersel' clean," she said, lowering the lamp. "And ..."

The sound of the little boy's crying drew her attention. With an angry snort, she pushed Jake out of the way and stood over the boy. Jake frowned when he saw her haul the squirming, yelping boy to his feet by one ear. "What are ye snivellin' about now, O'Donnell?" she shouted into the terrified boy's face.

Jake studied him. He had brown, curly hair and his face looked almost ghostly it was so pale. His big, brown eyes were wide with fear. "I ... I want me mammy," he cried.

"Yer mammy's dead!" shouted the Matron. "Dead. She died a week ago and yer still snivellin' about her. She's gone. She won't be back. Do ye understand? She won't ever come back. Now stop yer cryin' or I'll have ye put into the Punishment Room." Suddenly she let go of the boy's ear and slapped him. With a cry, he fell against the brick wall and slid onto his bed. The Matron glared at him. "If I hear any more about ye wantin' yer mammy, I'll have ye put into the Punishment Room and I'll throw away the key. Ye hear me? Do ye?"

"A ... aye, Matron," whispered the boy, tears bubbling on the edge of his eyes.

Jake could see he was trying hard to hold back his tears.

With another snort, the Matron turned to Jake. "You," she snapped. "Get to yer bed." She glared at the other boys nearest her. "Tomorrow, we're goin' to clean out this whole dormitory. Everythin' in it will be scrubbed down. I thought I saw a flea in O'Donnell's bed."

The boys' groans echoed around the dormitory.

"Now, if I hear any more noise or cryin' the night, it'll be all the worse fer yees." With that, the burly woman strode along the dormitory to the stairs. The boys waited until they heard the sound of her boots clatter down the stairs before sitting up.

"Oul' snotter," said a boy's voice.

"Aye, oul' green snotter," another boy said, suddenly laughing.

"Oul' green pig's snotter," another boy laughed. Several boys laughed at this.

"I'd like to slap her oul' bake," a boy said from further down the dormitory.

"Aye, and then ye'd end up in the infirmary," laughed a boy near Jake.

"It would be worth it," said the other boy.

"Would it? Don't ferget, she'd be the one lukin' after ye," another boy said. "She's as strong as a man, that one, don't ferget."

"She has muscles like a man, anyway," giggled a boy on the other side of the dormitory. "She's got a moustache like a man," laughed the same boy. Almost at once, the whole dormitory erupted into laughter.

Jake lay listening to their laughter, wondering how they could find anything to laugh at in the hellhole they lived in. He could see the boys fairly well by the light from narrow shafts of moonlight that shone through holes in the roof. He turned to look at the little boy beside him. He was about to speak to him when he heard noises behind him. He turned. Some boys were slipping towards them. Their faces became visible as they drew nearer. Ignoring Jake, the boys looked down at the little boy.

"It's yer fault, O'Donnell," snarled the biggest of the boys. He was broad-shouldered, with short black hair and a crooked nose. He kicked at the little boy's feet. "Now we have to clean up the dorm because of ye."

"I ... I'm sorry, McCallister," cried the little boy. "But it wasn't my fault. I didn't do anythin' ..."

"Ye wee skitter," shouted McCallister, suddenly reaching and pulling the frightened little boy to his feet. "Now yer goin' to pay fer annoyin' the Matron." He nodded to the three other boys and one of them grabbed the little boy's arm. Then they began to pull him past Jake and down the dormitory. They stopped at two beams that supported the main trusses on the right hand side of the path. Jake couldn't believe what he was seeing as they began to tie the struggling, crying boy to one of the beams. This had all happened in seconds and other boys had risen to watch. Horrified, Jake saw McCallister bunch his fists and with a loud curse, punch the little boy in the stomach. The boy gave a startled croak and doubled over. McCallister grinned at the other boys and raised his fist. "Are ye ready fer another one, O'Donnell?"

Suddenly, before he could stop himself, Jake was on his feet shouting, "Stop that!"

Everyone turned. All the boys gaped at Jake as he staggered down the dormitory towards McCallister. "Untie him," he shouted, glaring at one of the bully's cronies. The boy, who was slightly smaller than Jake, looked at McCallister, who was sizing up Jake.

"Why don't ye do it?" said McCallister quietly. He gritted his teeth when Jake pushed past the boys to reach for the thick twine that bound the little boy's arms to the hard beam. The frightened boy's eyes never left Jake as he began to untie him.

Suddenly McCallister swung a punch at Jake. It caught him high on his right cheek and, with a cry, he staggered back. "Get him!" shouted the bully.

Before Jake could defend himself, McCallister and his cronies had leapt, punching and tearing at him. But a shout from down the dormitory stopped them. "It's the Matron!"

In seconds the boys had scattered, leaving Jake lying on the floor. Dazed, he rose. He realised that if the Matron caught him or the little boy they'd be punished. He couldn't leave him tied up. In a moment he was untying the little boy and had him free. Then he half-carried him back to his bed and there they lay, hardly daring to breathe, waiting for the Matron to appear. A minute later it was obvious the shout had been a false alarm. Now McCallister's voice echoed up the dormitory. "We'll get ye again, O'Donnell, and yer new friend. We'll get yees. We have plenty of time. We'll get the pair of yees."

Jake frowned. He stared down the dormitory, but he couldn't see any boys on the path. Tenderly he touched his swollen cheek, then turned when he heard the little boy crying. "Ah, don't be afraid," he whispered. He turned to look down the dormitory again. "I don't think McCallister or any of the others will bother us the night. They're cowards. Don't be afraid," he repeated. At least I hope they don't bother us, he thought.

The boy turned. "Th ... thank you," he whispered.

"Don't worry about it," whispered Jake.

The boy was quiet for a few seconds as he studied Jake. "What's yer name?" he asked.

"Jake. Jake Miller. Yers?"

"David O'Donnell. You can call me Davey. Ahm, Jake?"

"Aye?"

"Is yer mammy still alive?"

"Aye, and me da."

"Me mammy died a week ago," said Davey. "They wouldn't let me see her. They said she had tie-foid or somethin' like that. It's a disease." Jake gulped. He knew about typhoid. "Me mammy's buried out the back with the other paupers."

"What's a pauper?" asked Jake.

"You are," said Davey. "We all are. We're poor. People with no money and nowhere to live are paupers. Jake?"

"Aye?"

"Is yer ma in here too?"

"Aye, and me da." Davey's next two words surprised Jake. "Yer lucky."

"Lucky?" he exclaimed.

"That they're alive and ye have a da too. I never knew me da. Jake?"

"Aye?"

"Do ... do ye believe in Heaven?"

"Heaven?" Jake frowned. "I never thought about it. Naw," he said sharply. "I don't."

"I do. I had a dream after me mammy died. I saw her as plain as day. She said she was watchin' over me and not to be afraid."

"Ach, sure that was only ..." Jake was about to tell Davey it was only a dream, but he stopped. Better to let the little fella believe. If it makes him happy, he thought.

"Jake?"

"Aye?"

"Will ... will ye be me friend? I don't have any friends in here."

"Friend? Aye, if ye like. I'll be yer friend."

"Thanks, Jake," whispered Davey. "Jake?"

"Aye?"

"Is yer face sore?"

Jake touched his bruise again. "Naw, it's all right. What about you?"

"McCallister beat me up before," said Davey. "I'm afraid of him. He can be very bad. Me mammy told me not to be afraid of him, but I am. I'm afraid of the dark too. The porter locked me in the Punishment Room fer six hours a few months ago. It was ... bad. I imagined all sorts of things. It's so dark in there. There was a big rat there. I couldn't see it but I knew it was there. I heard it. It crawled over me face once." Davey shuddered. "Jake, I think I'd die if I was put in the Punishment Room again."

"Don't worry, Davey," whispered Jake, smiling at him. "We'll luk after each other. We'll be all right." He wondered what the Punishment Room was like.

"Jake?"

"Aye?"

"Thanks fer bein' me friend."

Jake heard the little boy yawn. "Go to sleep, Davey," he whispered. "I'll see ye in the mornin'." Suddenly his stomach rumbled. He was ravenous. He lay now, thinking about his own predicament, resolving that, when he was strong enough, he would somehow get himself and his parents out of the

Workhouse. Later, as a shaft of moonlight shone between his and Davey's beds, he listened to boys talking

"When I get out of here, I'm never goin' to be hungry," said a boy three beds away. "I'm goin' to get a job, a good job."

"Aye, doin' what?" another boy said. "Ye've no trade."

"I'll get a job of some sort," answered the boy. "If I don't, maybe I'll stow away on a ship goin' to Canada or some place."

"Ye'll be hungry then, all right. It takes nearly two months to sail to Canada."

"It does not!"

"It does so!"

"Even if it does, I'll be all right."

"When me da gets better, we're gettin' out of here," another boy said quietly.

"Yer da's never goin' to get better."

"Aye he is!"

"He's not!"

"He is ..."

"Will yous two shut up!" a tired voice from further down the dormitory shouted. "I'm tryin' to sleep!"

"Shut up yersel'!" shouted another boy.

The thud as something hard flew up the dormitory echoed around them. The brief silence that followed soon became a snoring chorus and it was quite a while before Jake drifted away.

THE WOMEN'S WARD

Jake's mother lay awake in the women's ward. It was a long oblong room with many rough beds made of canvas and filled with straw lying on each side of the longest walls. The whitewashed walls were covered in damp, cracking blobs of plaster caused by earlier dampness when the water had run down the walls and seeped under the many coats of whitewash. There were no windows in the long ward and the high ceiling was criss-crossed with wide cracks.

Mary lay between two women. The younger, to her right, was coughing quietly, but every so often she would break into great fits of loud, wracking coughs. Mary shivered as she thought about Paddy and Jake, and suddenly she was crying.

"There, love," the woman with the cough whispered. "Don't ye be upsettin' yersel'." Still coughing quietly, she rose from her bed and crawled over to Mary. "Ye'll feel better in the mornin'. Ye'll soon get used to bein' in here."

She was the thinnest woman Mary had ever seen, and her greying hair hung straggled around her tiny face giving her a forlorn look. She wore a light shift that hung on her thin shoulders. Her pale face was furrowed with wrinkles, yet she was not much older than Mary.

"Aw aye, will she?" the woman on Mary's left said as she sat up. "I've never." She had short grey hair and bright intelligent blue eyes.

"Ach, Aggie, don't ye start yer moanin', fer God's sake. Can't ye see she's depressed enough? What's yer name, love? Mine's Lily Carlin. That crabbit oul' biddy beside ye is ... is called Aggie Moore." Lily began to cough again.

"Mary Miller." Sniffing, Mary dried her eyes. "Me and me husband Paddy, and Jake, our son ... Jake! Oh, God, I have to get to him. He'll be afraid." She moved to get out of bed.

"Easy, easy, love," coughed Lily, restraining her. "Ye'll not get near the boys' dormitory. They keep all the inmates apart at night. Ye'll see yer son at breakfast the morra. What happened to yees? How did yees land ... land ... in this godfersaken place?"

"The farmer threw us out of our cottage," explained Mary. "We hadn't even time to gather up any of our belongin's and we were robbed of what little savin's we had on the way to Derry. When we did get to Derry, we begged. But we couldn't get enough to feed us. We had to come into the Workhouse. If we hadn't, we would have died."

"I see ye had lice," said Aggie, nodding to Mary's shorn head.

Mary ran her fingers through her short hair. "We were covered in them," she whispered, and a tear rolled down her face.

"Is it just yersel', yer husband and yer ... yer ... son?" asked Lily. "Have ye no-one else who could ... could help ye?"

"No ..." Mary decided to trust the women. "We have a son in America. He emigrated with his wife." She began to cry again. "I begged Paddy to send word to him, but he wouldn't. He wouldn't even come to Derry to see Eamon off. Eamon, that's me eldest son's name. Anyway, we couldn't have got word to him. None of us can write. We could have got our neighbour Bridget to write a letter, but my Paddy's so proud, ye see. He'd never ask our Eamon fer help."

"Pride," snapped Aggie. "Hah! My oul' man was proud, and luk where it got us!"

"I wouldn't care what yer husband says, Mary. I would try and get a letter to yer son without him knowin'," said Lily hoarsely, suddenly turning sideways and spitting phlegm across the floor.

"Oh, I couldn't do that!" exclaimed Mary. "I couldn't go against Paddy. He'd never fergive me."

"No matter about him fergivin' ye," snorted Aggie.

"What's he like, yer eldest?" asked Lily.

Mary sighed. "Ah, he's handsome; like Paddy once was. He's strong, too, and gentle. His wife Ann is a lovely girl. They have a son, Patrick, and another wain on the way."

"Do ye have his address?" asked Lily.

"Aye."

"Mary, maybe ... maybe ... maybe we could help ye get a letter to yer son," said Lily.

"We!" snorted Aggie. "I like the way ye said 'we'. I'm the only one in the women's ward who can write, so how are ye goin' to get the letter written? Ye remember what happened the last time ye tried somethin' like that?"

Frowning, Mary looked at Lily. "They locked Aggie in the women's Punishment Room fer ... fer ... eight hours. Ach, but don't worry, Mary, we'll sort ... we'll sort ... somethin' out." Just then, Mary's stomach rumbled. The embarrassing noise seemed to go on for ever. "Hungry?" asked Lily.

"Starvin'," said Mary, holding her stomach as it rumbled again.

"It won't be long 'til the mornin'," said Lily. "Ye'll get fed then. I'll get back to me ... bed now. Don't worry, M ... Mary. There's worse things to worry about. Aye, plenty worse." Coughing, she crawled back to bed.

Minutes later, unable to sleep with Lily's persistent coughing, Mary whispered, "Lily, are ye awake?"

"Aye, love, I am. I hardly ... hardly sleep at all with this damned ... damned coughin'."

"Lily," whispered Mary, "how have ye stuck this place so long? I mean, what's kept ye goin'? I ... I need to know." She began to cry. "I don't think I'll be able to ..."

Coughing, Lily crawled back to Mary's bed and sat on the edge of it. "Mary," she whispered, "the tears will stop after a while. Ye'll soon learn ... learn to accept livin' here. And Mary, please take my advice, don't, fer God's sake, let yer husband or yer son see ye cryin'. It'll ... it'll ... only make it all the worse fer them. Ye'll just have to keep goin' fer their sakes ... as well as yer own. In the mornin' ye'll see them at breakfast. Don't let them see yer beaten. Don't, fer God's sake, worry yer husband into a ... into an early ... early grave."

Mary studied Lily for a few seconds as she broke into another fit of coughing. "Lily," she whispered when it had eased, "how long have ye been in the Workhouse?"

Still coughing, Lily turned away from her. "Seven years and seven months and ... a long time. A long ... long time."

"What happened?" asked Mary. "How did ye come to be in here?"

Lily turned. "It's not much of a story." Mary raised her eyebrows to indicate she would like to hear it. "Me husband left me," Lily said quickly, coughing again. "Me and the wains. He buggered off to Scotland when ... when things got tough. Ah, they were always tough. Me youngest, Lillian, was five months old. We'd no money and we were starvin'. The police were sent to Scotland to bring me husband back when we landed in here. When they found him, he was nearly ... nearly dead with the drink. They brought him back, but he died a month later. I knew then we'd be ... we'd be here fer for ever."

"Where are yer wains now?" asked Mary.

"Paul's in the boys' dormitory." Lily stared at the floor. Her next words shocked Mary. "Kevin and Lillian died."

"Died!" gasped Mary. "Oh, Lily."

"Aye," whispered Lily with tears in her eyes. "Wee Kevin died a few months after Lillian. There was ... was ... was a lot of disease goin' about then. More than now."

"Lily," whispered Mary, reaching out to touch her arm. "I'm so sorry."

"Aye, well, don't be," snapped the older woman pulling away. "Ye'll have yer own troubles ahead of ye. Luk, Mary, just remember what I ... what I told ye. Don't worry yer husband sick. Remember."

"Aye, Lily, I will," said Mary, smiling at her. "Ye'd better get back to bed. Ye'll get yer death." She shivered. "Is it always as cold as this?"

"Aye, it is," said Lily as she crawled back to bed. "But it's better than bein' ... bein' outside and left to the elements. Night, Mary," she whispered, pushing down hard into her bed as the coughing grew worse.

"Night, Lily," whispered Mary. She lay listening to Lily and thinking about the terrible life the woman had had. It was quite a while before her tiredness overcame the sound of Lily's harsh coughing and she fell asleep.

THE PUNISHMENT ROOM

It was Reggie, the porter's assistant, shouting and kicking at the feet of those boys unfortunate enough to have them sticking out into the pathway, that woke Jake. It was still dark and feeling very weak, he staggered to his feet. A groan from Davey had him turning to him. The little boy was bent over and holding his stomach. "Davey, are ye all right?" Jake whispered, reaching out to him.

"Aye," grunted the little boy, straightening. "Me belly's a bit sore, but not as bad as the last time that big gulpin' gave me a doin'."

Seeing Davey was all right, Jake looked down the dormitory. "What do we do now, Davey?" he whispered.

"Wait 'til Reggie takes us down to the dinin' hall," replied Davey.

Three minutes later, Reggie led the boys in single file down the stairs, along a dark narrow corridor and into the dining hall. This was the biggest place in the Workhouse. It was where the inmates were fed. The men and women were already there at the back of the hall, men on one side and women on the other, all standing beside long benches. In front of the benches were low wooden tables. Shortly after the boys arrived to stop at the left side of the hall, the Matron led about ninety girls to the right side.

At the very top of the hall, near the door, was a dais. On the dais were a stool and a waist-high podium on which sat an open prayer book and a thick Bible.

Jake looked around for his father. At first he couldn't see him, but, as he searched along the rows of men, he saw a stooped, bald-headed figure near one end. Shocked, he realised it was his father. Jake was so upset by his father's appearance that he began to push past some boys to get over to him.

Whack! The slap on the back of his head stopped him. It was Reggie. "Where do ye think yer goin', Miller?" he snapped, grabbing Jake by the arm. "Get back in the queue."

"I ... I only want to speak to me da," said Jake, holding his head.

"Lissen, Miller," snarled the porter's assistant, looking around. "Get to the back of the queue and stand in it 'til I tell ye to sit down." He gritted his teeth and hissed, "Do ye hear me?"

Sniffing back a tear, Jake glanced at McCallister, who made a face at him. "Aye, I hear ye," he muttered, moving to go to the back of the queue.

"I'll get ye the night, Miller," whispered the bully as Jake was about to pass. "I'm goin' to give ye the hammerin' of yer life. You and that wee skitter O'Donnell."

At the mention of Davey, Jake stopped and glared at McCallister. He was about to say, *leave Davey alone*, when Reggie hissed, "Miller, get to the back of the queue!"

"The night," whispered McCallister, raising his fist as Jake walked on.

"You all right, Jake?" asked Davey when Jake reached him.

"Aye, I'm all right," said Jake, looking back at his father. He turned to look for his mother and spotted her right away. She was smiling over at him. Jake was even more shocked by his mother's appearance. His heart was pounding, but he managed to smile back.

"Silence!" shouted the porter when the Master appeared. The hubbub of noise stopped and only Lily's harsh coughing could be heard as the Master strode to the dais. He is the devil, thought Jake as the Master glared around the eight hundred inmates. Everyone except Jake bent their heads. The Master's eyes narrowed when he saw Jake's defiance, but seconds later he began prayers.

When the service was over, Jake looked again for his mother. Her head was bowed and she looked so lost and fragile that suddenly he had to hug her and tell her they would be all right. Tears filled his eyes, and before he realised it, he was pushing through the boys towards her. "Ma!" he cried. "Ma!"

Startled, his mother looked around.

"Tell him to go back," hissed Aggie. "Quick. He'll get in trouble."

But it was too late. For just as Jake reached her, the porter and his assistant grabbed him. "Where do ye think yer goin', Miller?" snarled the porter.

"Let me go!" shouted Jake.

"What is all this?" shouted the Master as he pushed roughly past two girls towards the struggling Jake.

"Sir," said the porter, nodding to Jake.

The Master studied Jake, his eyes narrowing. "Miller," he said, spitting out the words. "I told ye ye would see yer parents at breakfast. I did not say ye could speak to them." He gritted his teeth when he saw Jake put up a fresh struggle.

"Let me go!" shouted Jake. "Let me go!" At the same time, his mother was trying to pull away from Lily and Aggie to go to her son, but she was too weak.

Crack! The slap threw Jake's head back. Immediately the porter and his assistant let him go. Jake glared at the Master's hateful face. The Master had slapped him and suddenly, before he had time to think, he took two steps towards him and, with an angry cry, slapped the Master as hard as he could.

Shocked, the Master staggered back and almost fell. And for a few seconds, no-one breathed. Everyone was as shocked as the Master. Suddenly, the porter punched Jake on the back of his head and he fell to the ground. The porter and Reggie grabbed him again and hauled him to his feet by the arms. Dazed, Jake heard the Master scream, "Hold him! Hold the brat! Hold him!"

Slap! Slap! Slap! Slap!

The sound of the Master slapping Jake's face echoed around the hall, and just before Jake passed out, he thought he heard his mother scream his name.

"Oh boy," hissed the porter as he and his assistant dragged Jake along the floor. "Ye made a mistake, Miller, a big mistake. Yer marked now. Marked."

Jake recovered just when the porter dropped his arm. He raised his head to stare up at a broad, black oak door in front of him. "Get him to his feet," hissed the porter to Reggie as he unlocked the door with a big black key. The door creaked open. As it did, a musty smell from inside hit Jake as the porter turned to him. Jake stared into the narrow room and the darkness, and now he remembered Davey's words, *"I'd die if I was locked in there again."*

Suddenly, with a blow on the back of his neck from the porter's assistant, Jake was forced inside. "We'll see how smart ye are when ye get out!" shouted the porter. "If ye get out." With a curse, he slammed the door shut.

The darkness was more than enough to frighten Jake, for it was so dark he couldn't see anything, not even a chink of light through the door. He couldn't even see the door. And when he held his hand up to his face, he couldn't see it. He stared down, trying to see the floor and then began to feel for the walls. Reaching out, he moved forward. As he did, something rolled under his left foot, something hard. A pebble? Suddenly his hands were touching the cold, damp wall and he could feel the lime mortar in the joints between the bricks. Like fine sand, he felt some of it dust onto his hands. He turned to his left and edged along until his hands touched that wall. Seconds later, he realised that the room was only about as long as himself and twice as wide. He couldn't see where the door was, but he knew it was in front of him.

Before long, he was sitting on his hunkers with his back to the wall. His stomach rumbled again. He hadn't had anything to eat. "Stupid!" he shouted, angry with himself. "Stupid!" *I shouldn't have slapped the Master. No, I'm not stupid.* "He deserved it!" he screamed. "He shouldn't have hit me!" He slid his feet out and sat on the cold floor. A noise to his left soon attracted his attention, a scuffling noise. He held his breath and listened. Nothing. With a sigh, he expelled his breath. All of a sudden, he felt sick with hunger and he began to wonder how long he would be locked up. Davey said he'd been locked in the room for six hours. Poor wee Davey, he thought. It must have been a terrible nightmare for him. He thought about McCallister. If he harms Davey, I'll get him. But now his thoughts drifted to his mother and, all of a sudden, he began to cry. He wanted to protect her. He knew she would be worried about him. "Ma!" he cried. "Oh, ma!"

Later, weak with hunger, he drifted to sleep, thinking about Eamon and the happy times at home.

THE RAT

The gnawing at his head woke him an hour later. "The rat!" he screamed, pushing at the soft furry creature and, with a screech, it scuttled away. Shuddering, Jake felt the cut on his head. It was wet. "Blood!" he gasped. "It's blood! *My* blood!" The rat had been nibbling at the cut on his head. Blood trickled down the back of his head as he scrambled to his feet and, suddenly dizzy, he had to lean against the wall for support. As his head swam, he listened. A squeal to his left made him kick out and he almost fell. No wonder Davey was afraid, he thought. Jake had never been frightened of rats, for he had seen many around the farm, but here, alone in the inky darkness, he felt vulnerable.

He wondered how long he had been asleep. He reckoned he had been in the room for four, maybe five, hours. His stomach rumbled continually now and he slowly slid down the wall onto his hunkers again. He sniffed. There was a smell in the cold room. He didn't want to think what the smell was. He listened again for the rat, wondering how big it was. It must have seemed gigantic to wee Davey. But how was it able to get in and out of the Punishment Room? It had to be able to get out, he thought. If it couldn't, it would have starved.

Other horrifying thoughts occurred to him and he felt the skin prickle along the back of his neck. What if there was more than one rat? What if he was too weak to fight them off? He would be eaten alive. The rats would have the advantage in the dark. Even one rat would be a danger.

A noise to his right had him standing up again and he kicked out in that direction. A sudden squeak to his left had his heart pounding with fear. "Ahhhh!" he shouted, as he kicked again. "Ahhhh! Get away! Get away! Ahhhh!" He kicked and flailed his arms for over a minute, screaming all the time until, exhausted and sobbing, he slid back down the wall onto his bottom. "Eamon," he cried, "where are ye? Where are ye?" Somehow, an hour or so later, he fell asleep.

He woke with a start. Something had crawled across his mouth. "Ahhhh!" he screamed, brushing at his mouth. He pulled himself up again. The sudden movement had him fighting nausea and he swayed and almost fell. He widened his eyes and tried to see but it was dark, much darker than before, and he began to cry again. Surely they'll not keep me here much longer, he thought. I must be in here over twelve hours, no ... longer. "Oh God!" he cried. "I'm so hungry. So very hungry." Unable to stay on his feet, he slumped to the floor. Shivering uncontrollably, he pulled his knees up to his face, then suddenly stiffened when he heard scuffling to his left. "Get away!" he screamed. "Get away! Get awayyyy! Let me out! Please! Let me out!"

Holding on to the wall, he rose to his feet again and began to search for the door, but he couldn't find it. "Please!" he cried. "Let me out." Once more he slid to the ground to pull his knees up to his face. "Please," he whimpered, tears running down his face into his open mouth.

In the next six hours, Jake nodded off several times only to waken with a start as the fear of the rats trembled through him. But soon he became too weak to care. He realised long ago that he had wet himself. He sat in the cold, his urine stinging his legs, too tired and too hungry to care any more what happened to him.

***

He woke to the sound of the door opening. Aware of something black scurrying away into the darker part of the room, Jake stared up at the porter's assistant.

"The Master wants to see ye," snarled Reggie. "Get up." He kicked out at Jake's legs as Jake struggled to get to his feet. "Miller," snarled Reggie, kicking again at Jake's legs. "On yer feet. Now! The Master's waitin'. On yer feet!"

Jake had never felt so weak in all his young life and, feeling nauseous, he used the wall to get to his feet. Halfway up the hall, Reggie hissed, "Miller, will ye hurry up! The Master's waitin'."

The Master was standing by his desk. He gritted his teeth when he saw the condition Jake was in as he staggered into the room. Jake blinked and tried to hold his head up to stare at the Master. "Wait outside," snapped the Master to Reggie. The porter's assistant glanced at Jake, then left the room.

Jake swayed, his face paler than before, as he looked at the Master, who seemed to float across the room towards him.

"Miller," the Master hissed. "Ye struck me." His eyes burned into Jake. "Ye struck the Master. Ye shouldn't have done that."

With a great effort, Jake raised his head and stared into the Master's hateful face.

"I want to know now, Miller, if ye intend to strike me again," said the Master. "Do ye?"

Jake stood as erect as he could and was about to say, *if ye slap me again, I'll slap ye back*. But when the Master hissed, "Do ye want to spend another twelve hours in the Punishment Room?" he gave a start. Twelve hours, he thought. Was that all the time I've been in the Punishment Room? Twelve hours? It had seemed like a day... or longer.

"Miller, I asked ye a question!" shouted the Master, bunching his fists.

"No," whispered Jake.

"No, what?" shouted the Master.

"I ... I don't ..."

Crack! The sound of the hard slap echoed around the room. The Master stepped quickly back and glared at Jake, who had been stunned by the blow but had not fallen.

"I asked ye a question, Miller!" shouted the Master, taking a step towards Jake. "Do ye want to spend more time in the Punishment Room?"

"No," whispered Jake.

Crack! The second slap shook him and he fell backwards onto the floor. The Master seemed to glide above him. "Are ye sure, Miller?" he asked, bunching his fists again.

"A ... aye," gasped Jake as stars floated in front of his eyes.

"What? What did ye say?" asked the Master, tilting his head.

"Stand up! Stand up and address me properly. Stand up!" he shouted, his face red with anger.

Grunting, Jake managed to get to his feet.

"I asked ye, Miller," snarled the Master, his face inches from Jake's as spittle and foam splashed into it. "Are ye sure ye don't want to spend more time in the Punishment Room?"

"Aye ... sir, I'm sure," cried Jake, tears filling his eyes. "I'm sorry ..."

"What? What did ye say?" shouted the Master.

"I'm sorry, sir. I'm really sorry."

The Master seemed about to turn away, but was really preparing to strike Jake again. His hard slap threw Jake back across the room and he hit the door and slid to the floor. "Oh, ye'll be sorry, all right!" shouted the Master. "Porter! Porter!" Immediately, Reggie came into the room, sliding Jake backwards as he opened the door. "Take this wastrel to the dining hall. Have him clean the floor 'til suppertime. And if it isn't cleaned to your satisfaction, he's to get nothin' to eat 'til the mornin'."

Jake was too dazed to get to his feet, but the assistant porter hauled him up by one arm. With tears streaming down his face, Jake heard the Master shout, "I told ye yer insolence would soon be stamped out in the Workhouse! Ah, get him out of me sight. Any more trouble from him, see that he spends a full day in the Punishment Room."

"Boy," hissed Reggie as he half-dragged Jake along the hall. "Ye'd be better to keep out of the Master's way from now on. A day in the Punishment Room will seem like a holiday to what he'll do to ye if ye bother him again." He studied Jake. He could see he was weak. "When was the last time ye ate?"

Jake frowned. He couldn't remember.

"Well, supper is at eight o'clock. Ye'll scrub the dining-hall floor 'til then. And ye heard the Master; if it's not spotless, ye'll get no supper."

Just then, the porter arrived.

"Takin' him to the dinin' hall, sir," said Reggie. "Scrubbin'."

"When ye get him the bucket and stuff, come out to the yard. I need ye there," said the porter and then strode off.

When they reached the dining hall, Jake saw two women scrubbing the floor of the dais. One of them was coughing.

"Stand there, Miller, and don't move. I'll get ye water, a bucket and a brush. Don't move, ye hear me?" snapped Reggie.

When he was gone, Jake saw one of the women straighten and rub her back. His eyes widened when he saw it was his mother. He was about to shout to her when he heard Reggie returning. "Right, Miller. Start in that corner near the door." He handed Jake a bucket of cold water and a wooden scrubbing brush. "I'll want to see that whole corner scrubbed when I return. If it's not clean enough, ye'll get no supper." With that, he left the hall.

Jake carried the bucket to the corner of the room and looked behind to make sure Reggie had gone. "Ma," he whispered. "Ma."

His mother turned. "Jake!" she cried, getting to her feet. In seconds she was hugging Jake as tears ran down their faces. Coughing, Lily now stood at the door keeping watch.

Jake quickly explained the horror of the Punishment Room, but he didn't tell his mother about the Master's treatment of him after, because he didn't want to worry her. When he was finished, his mother whispered, "Jake, please, no more trouble. I don't want ye to get hurt, or worse."

Jake sighed. "How's me da?"

"I ... I don't know," whispered his mother. "I've seen him at breakfast, but we're not allowed to speak to each other."

"Ma," whispered Jake, turning to look at Lily. "Are we ever goin' to get out of this place? I don't think that ... I ..." A tear rolled down his face.

"Jake," said his mother, smiling as she remembered Lily's advice. "Don't worry. We'll get out of here. Ye'll see. It's not so bad if ye give no trouble. Promise me, no more trouble. Do as yer told. Please, Jake, promise me. No more trouble."

Just then, Lily turned. "There's ... there's someone comin'." Coughing, she hurried up the hall to the dais.

"Promise," whispered Jake's mother as she hurried after her.

"I promise," whispered Jake, dropping to his knees to scrub furiously at the floor. He was just in time, for the Matron and her assistant came into the hall. They stood at the door, looking at Jake's mother and Lily. Lily had broken into another fit of coughing and Jake listened as the assistant whispered to the Matron, "She's got consumption. She'll not last the month." Jake realised they were talking about Lily.

"Not with that cough," whispered the Matron. "Bring her to me after supper fer an examination." The two women watched Lily for a few seconds, then left the hall.

Jake sighed and began to scrub as hard as he could to finish the corner. He didn't want to miss supper. His mouth began to water at the thought of something to eat. But now, he began to think about McCallister and his threat.

A New Friend

As Jake lined up in the dining room with the other boys for supper, Davey whispered to him. "Are ye all right, Jake?"

Jake nodded, for he was too weak to talk and he didn't want to frighten Davey.

"Did the big rat come?" whispered Davey, looking in the direction of the porter's assistant.

Jake's mouth began to water when he saw the huge pot of porridge. As he came up to it, a boy filled his wooden plate with a ladle. Jake's hands were shaking so much he was afraid to drop his plate, so he tucked it tight to his chest as he walked to the table.

"Did the rat come?" Davey asked again as he followed Jake.

"Aye," said Jake, unable to say any more as he hurried to the table. He thought he would never reach it. Quarts of buttermilk in huge mugs sat in each boy's space at the table, and Jake was about to eat when Davey stopped him. He nodded to Reggie. The porter's assistant was staring along the table. No boy was allowed to eat until Reggie gave the word.

"Right," he said. "Ye may begin."

Jake gulped a quick mouthful of buttermilk and began to eat his porridge; he didn't stop until the plate was clean. Holding the plate to his mouth, he began to lick it. As he did, he didn't see Reggie rising and coming towards him. Smack! The slap on the back of his head made his mouth hit the plate and it dropped with a clatter to the table.

"Miller! In here, ye use a spoon," snarled Reggie, glancing at the porter glaring over at them.

"Aye, sir," said Jake quickly. "Sorry, sir."

When Reggie went back to the head of the table, Jake reached for the rest of his buttermilk. By the end of supper, he was feeling much better.

***

Later that night in the dormitory, Davey whispered to Jake, "Ye'll feel better after a while. I was tired when I got out. Jake, was ... was the rat big? Was it? I imagined it as big as a cat. Was it?"

"Naw," replied Jake, not wanting to frighten Davey. "It was only a wee thing, about the size of a mouse. It might even have been a mouse." He touched the congealed blood on his head.

"It was bigger than a ..." began Davey. Jake frowned when he saw Davey cower back.

"So ye found out what it was like in the Punishment Room, Miller." It was McCallister, and behind him stood his three cronies. Jake sat up as Davey cowered closer to the wall. "I said I'd get ye, Miller," snarled McCallister. He turned to his cronies. "Get him to his feet and tie him to the wood."

Jake was shocked at how weak he was, for the three boys easily overpowered him and he was half-dragged, half-carried along the path to the beam.

"Now, Miller," growled McCallister as Jake was being tied to the beam with his face to it. "I'm goin' to teach ye who's the top dog in this dorm." He looked at the other boys as they gathered around.

Jake turned his head. He frowned when he saw McCallister being handed a piece of rope with a huge knot tied on one end of it. The bully turned. "O'Donnell!" he shouted. "When we're done with yer friend, yer next." He grinned.

At this, Jake got very angry, for he knew Davey would be frightened. "McCallister," he said quietly, "if I was stronger, I'd fight ye. Yer a coward. I know it." The bully's face darkened. "I dare ye to fight me, McCallister," said Jake. Around him, he heard the gasps of some of the boys. At least I'll have a chance if I fight him, he thought. He didn't think he could defeat McCallister, but it would be better than being tied to a beam and beaten.

Suddenly, McCallister swung the knotted rope at him. The shock of pain as the knot thudded into his lower back had Jake gasping aloud.

"Go on, Con," one of the bully's cronies hissed. "Give it to him again."

"Yer afraid to fight me," grunted Jake, trying to turn to face the bully. "One to one." Grinding his teeth, McCallister raised his arm to hit Jake again.

"Maybe ye are afraid, McCallister," said a voice from one of the boys gathered behind him.

Scowling, McCallister turned quickly. Lowering the rope, he snarled, "Who said that?"

Jake and all the boys gaped when they saw a lanky boy push through to stand between McCallister and Jake. Jake recognised him as the boy who had led him to his bed last night. "I did," said the boy, looking straight into McCallister's angry face.

"Carlin," snarled the bully. "Who asked ye to butt yer nose in?"

Carlin, still looking him straight in the eyes, said, "Are ye afraid to fight him?" Carlin's thick eyebrows rose with the question. All the boys looked at McCallister, waiting for his answer.

"One to one," said Carlin. "A fair fight."

McCallister studied Jake.

"Surely yer not afraid?" said Carlin.

"I'm afraid of no-one," snarled the bully.

"Then fight him. A fair fight. One to one," said Carlin.

McCallister studied Jake again. "One to one," he muttered, and suddenly he was back home and his father was punching him in the chest.

"Hit me back! Go on, coward! Hit me! Hit me!"

"Naw, da! Please. I don't want to."

"Coward! Yer a coward! Hit me, I said!"

"Please, da. I don't want to. Please, don't make me."

"I won't have a coward fer a son! Hit me! Hit me back!"

"Da, please. I don't want to. Please, don't make me."

"Con, please. Leave him alone," cried his mother.

"He's a coward! I won't have a coward fer a son. I said, HIT ME!"

"Con, please, don't ..."

"Shut up, you! Shut up, I say!"

"Da, don't hit her! Da! Ma!"

Carlin's repeated question brought him back.

"Well, McCallister, are ye goin' to fight him, one to one?"

The bully studied Jake again. He could see Jake was weak. He looked around the boys again. They'll think I'm a coward if I don't, he thought. "All right, Carlin." Turning to one of his cronies, he snapped, "Untie him, Doherty." Then he moved back. "And give us room!" he shouted, glaring at Jake. "Miller, I'm goin' to give ye the beatin' of yer life. Ye'll be sorry ye never chose the rope."

Doherty, a boy with buckteeth, grinned as he untied Jake. "Ye'll be sorry," he hissed. "Con will kill ye." He moved back as Jake pulled the twine from his wrists. As Jake stepped away from the beam, McCallister, with a bellow, suddenly lowered his head and butted Jake in the stomach. Taken by surprise, Jake was forced back against the wall. "Go on, Con!" shouted Doherty. "Give it to him! Kick his head in!"

Jake knew as he struggled to keep the bigger boy away that he had to beat him. Even if he had been as strong as he was back at the cottage, he would not have been a match for the bully. A fist thudded against his bruised ribs and he gasped with the pain. But as McCallister moved in to punch harder, Jake fell towards him and wrapped his arms around the bully, locked his fingers and held the struggling, angry McCallister tight, preventing him from hitting him. Suddenly, because of McCallister's greater weight and strength, Jake lost his balance and they fell to the floor near the beam. As they did, Jake still held on. And as they rolled over and over, the back of Jake's head hit the beam. The bang caused Jake's head to bounce forward into McCallister's nose and, dazed, he released the bully.

McCallister, tasting the blood in his mouth, rose to his feet and, touching his nose, he stared at the blood on his hand. "Me nose," he groaned. "Ye broke it." Blood trickled into his mouth and he spluttered and spat. By then, Jake was back on his feet. Swaying, he bunched his fists, waiting for McCallister to attack again.

Suddenly, Doherty darted in from Jake's left side and hit him a low blow in the stomach. With a groan, Jake sank slowly to his knees. As he did, he heard Doherty moan loudly and Carlin shout, "I said, one to one!" Raising his head, Jake saw Doherty lying on the floor holding his eye and Carlin standing over him. "Touch him again," he shouted, "and I'll flatten ye!"

Everyone now turned to McCallister. He was still staring at the blood on his hands. The taste of it in his mouth was turning his stomach. "Ye broke me nose, Miller," he cried.

"Aye!" shouted Jake, scrambling to his feet and almost falling again. "And when I'm stronger, I'll break yer neck if ye touch Davey again."

McCallister studied Jake and, all of a sudden, the fight went out of him. He spat blood onto the floor and then, as he looked around the boys, his stomach heaved again. "This isn't over yet, Miller," he muttered, turning away. The other boys gaped at the bully as he walked to his bed muttering, "Ye broke me nose."

Carlin then went over to Jake. "His nose isn't broken," he said. "He'll be all right in the mornin'. But watch out fer him from now on. He'll be out fer revenge."

Jake smiled at him. "Thanks," he whispered as the other boys headed for their beds. "What's yer name?"

"Paul Carlin."

"I'm Jake Miller."

"I'll see ye the morra. At the yard probably," said Paul.

"At the yard?" said Jake.

"Aye. Ye'll be put to breakin' stones with the bigger boys and the men." Paul turned. "I'll see ye then."

"Aye, see ye then, Paul. And thanks again," said Jake. Paul waved, and then both he and Jake headed back to their beds.

When Jake returned, Davey whispered, "Did he hurt ye, Jake?"

"Naw."

"I was afraid fer ye."

"Don't worry about me," said Jake as he lay back. He grunted. His ribs still hurt. "Do ye know Paul Carlin?" he asked.

"He's been here since I came," said Davey. "He keeps 'til himself." Davey smiled. "I'm glad he helped ye."

"So am I," muttered Jake. He lay, exhausted and still hungry, thinking about the fight and his new friend until he drifted to sleep.

WORRYING TIMES

Next morning after breakfast, Jake was taken with Paul, McCallister and seven other boys out to the yard. Jake looked around the big yard. He could see a huge pile of large rocks at one end of it and several men were getting ready to begin breaking them. Jake's father was not there and he wondered where he was. At the other end of the yard, near the high wall that surrounded it, was a bigger pile of smaller stones. Two barrows were positioned by the large rocks, and leaning against the barrows were some block hammers and two huge sledgehammers.

"Miller, you and Carlin will do the barrowin' today, and when yer stronger, ye'll be put to breakin' the rocks," said Reggie.

As Paul and Jake walked to the bottom of the yard, Paul, with a grin on his face, whispered, "Barrowin's the easiest job."

But it was not as easy as he said. All that morning, Jake and Paul barrowed the smaller stones up to the pile at the top of the yard. It was also Jake and Paul's job to load the barrows using flat shovels.

Later, near dinnertime, as they trundled their barrows up the yard, Jake noticed that Paul was in a quiet, thoughtful mood. "What's wrong, Paul?" he asked.

Paul frowned. "Nothin'." he said quietly. Jake shrugged. It was Paul's business whatever was wrong. "Me ma's very sick," said Paul suddenly.

Jake noticed the tears in his eyes. "What's wrong with her?" he asked.

"Her chest ... lungs," said Paul. "Her coughin's got worse."

"Coughin'?" Jake remembered the woman with his mother in the dining hall.

"She's not gettin' any better," said Paul. He looked at Jake. "Jake, I ... I don't know what I'll do if anythin' happens to her. I ..." Paul thought now about his dead brother, Kevin, and baby sister, Lillian. He hadn't had time to get to know his little sister when she got sick and died. If his mother died, how would he cope? He knew he couldn't.

"Hey, you two, hurry up!" yelled one of the men. "The porter will be here soon."

"Ah, she'll be all right, Paul," whispered Jake as they hurried down the yard. Paul said nothing and Jake wondered how *he* would feel if his mother was sick. He remembered now the conversation between the Matron and the other woman, and he thought it must have been Paul's mother they had been talking about.

Later, as they queued for dinner, McCallister bumped against Jake purposely. "We're not finished yet, Miller," he snarled.

Jake shook his head. "No, I suppose not," he said quietly. "But I'll tell ye this, McCallister. Yer fight is with me, not wee Davey. With me. Ye hear?"

The bully scowled. "If I get a chance, I'll fix that wee skitter and I'll get me chance at ye, Miller. Ye can bet on it. Ye'll never know what hit ye when I do." Suddenly, he pushed past Jake. "Out of me way." As he did, Paul looked back and winked at Jake. Jake shook his head at him, nodded to the bully, and raised his eyebrows.

"What was it like, Jake?" asked Davey when Jake joined him.

"Breakin' rocks? I was barrowin'," answered Jake. "All right. The work wasn't that hard. I've worked harder on the farm." He studied the little boy. "What about you? What do ye do?"

"I mend shoes. I'm gettin' good at it," said Davey. "I like workin' with leather. I ..."

"Move along there," barked Reggie, pushing Davey in the back.

As they ate, Jake looked around for his parents. He had seen his mother earlier and she had smiled at him, but his father hadn't even looked in his direction.

That evening after supper, Jake was ready for McCallister and his cronies to start something, but when he saw that Paul had changed beds with another boy and was lying nearby, he relaxed. It was a warning to McCallister that he had two to deal with. The bully didn't bother him that night. Or the next. And so, Jake's life in the Workhouse passed with harder work breaking rocks every day in the yard. During the long nights when he was alone, Jake would often think about Eamon. How was he doing? He thought about Patrick, his nephew. What was he like?

New Birth and a Death

"It's a girl!" exclaimed Mrs Cartwright when she came out of the room carrying the small bundle. Eamon reached to see, but the kind woman said, "You'll see her later when she's more presentable. Go on in. Ann's waiting for you." She smiled, then hurried into the kitchen.

"Congratulations, Eamon," said Jack, reaching to take his hand.

Eamon smiled. "Thanks, Jack."

Cartwright nodded. "You'd better go in."

Ann reached to hug him as he came into the room. "A girl," said Eamon, smiling.

"Yer not disappointed then?" asked Ann, studying his face.

"Disappointed? I'm delighted. What are we goin' to call her?"

"Well, I thought Mary, after yer mother," said Ann.

"Mary," said Eamon, and suddenly he grew so sad that tears bubbled on the edge of his eyes.

"What is it?"

"I wish she was here to see her granddaughter," said Eamon, almost choking to keep from crying.

Their lives had improved a lot since they had first landed in Philadelphia. Ann was being taught to read and write by Mrs Cartwright. The Cartwrights, especially Mrs Cartwright, who was a small, neat woman with sparkling blue eyes and short, wavy, grey-blonde hair, had taken to the family right from the start. Mrs Cartwright doted on Patrick and, for a while, Ann had been able to take on a part-time job while Mrs Cartwright looked after him. Jack had admitted to Eamon that he was glad his wife had Patrick to look after. His wife had never got over the death of their son – until recently. He had told Eamon he was grateful to him. When Mrs Cartwright found out Ann couldn't write, she at once volunteered to teach her. And a few weeks later, Ann showed Eamon the letter she had drafted to send to his parents.

Now Eamon looked at his wife, who had fallen asleep. Their lives were complete. He had a well-paid job and a new baby. Yet, once more, he was thinking about his family back in Derry and how he missed them.

***

A month later, in the dormitory, Paul slipped over to Jake's bed. He told Jake that Father Duffy had been to see his mother. Father Duffy was a priest from the Waterside parish who was sometimes allowed into the Workhouse to minister to those who were dying.

"Jake," whispered Paul, checking to see if Davey was asleep. "She's dyin'. Me ma's dyin'." He began to cry.

With tears in his eyes, Jake tried to comfort Paul, saying, "Ah, she'll be all right, Paul. Don't worry." But he, too, knew what the priest's visit meant.

When Paul returned to his bed, he lay worrying about his mother. He ached to go to her, to hold her. Tears streamed down the sides of his face as he thought about her. He felt so helpless and angry at the hopelessness of it all.

***

Two nights later, Mary, who was kneeling beside Lily's bed, whispered, "Aggie, we should get the Matron."

"No!" gasped Lily. "No, Mary, please. I'll only be shifted to the infirmary. I'd ... I'd ... rather be here with yees."

"But, Lily ..." began Aggie.

"Please. I'm all right here. I'll ... I'll ... be leavin' yees soon anyway."

At this, Aggie gave a sob. "Ah, Lily, don't say that. Please, don't say that ..." A tear rolled down her worried face. What would she do without Lily? she thought. She was the only real friend she had. Who would listen to her and be nice to her? Who would give her hope? She remembered telling Lily in the early days that she had decided to kill herself. This was shortly after her husband had died. Lily had been understanding. She had told her she had felt the same way when Lillian and Kevin had died, but she had gone on for Paul's sake. There was always hope, she had told her.

Lily smiled. "Aggie, the hard one. Ye always tried to hide yer ... yer ... feelin's, but I knew what ye were like, didn't I?" She turned to Mary. "Mary, I ... I've ... somethin' to tell ye. I asked Father Duffy to promise me he would post a ... post a letter to yer son."

"A letter!" exclaimed Mary. She glanced at Aggie. "To Eamon? What letter? How did ye get Eamon's address?"

Lily coughed before answering. "I slipped it from yer belongin's one day when you and the others were down at dinner." She smiled at Mary's astonished face. "Father ... Father Duffy couldn't refuse a dyin' woman's wish, now, could he?"

"But how did ye write the letter, Lily?" asked Mary. "I mean, ye can't write."

Lily looked at Aggie and smiled. Mary turned to her.

"I'll deny it if the Master finds out," said Aggie. "I'll say yees forced me. I'll ... I'll ..."

Mary touched her hand and smiled. "Thanks, Aggie."

Suddenly Lily began another spate of coughing. Mary studied her. "Aggie," she whispered. "I don't care what she says. I'm goin' fer the Matron."

Lily, still coughing, reached to stop her. "No. Please, Mary. Stay here with me. Don't ... don't ... don't leave me alone. Please." Mary looked anxiously at Aggie. After another fit of coughing, and when she could speak, Lily whispered, "I saw him last night."

Mary frowned as she glanced at Aggie. "Who, Lily? Who did ye see? Father Duffy?"

"Me husband," said Lily.

"Yer husband!" exclaimed Aggie, glancing at Mary.

"Aye," Lily whispered hoarsely. "He came to the side of me bed. He was smilin' too. He usen't to smile much. Ah, he luked so handsome too. Like before, when we were married ... at the start. He said he was sorry fer leavin' me and the wains. He asked me to ... to fergive him." Lily's eyes filled with tears and she suddenly sobbed. "I never did, ye know. But I do now. I missed him, but I never fergive him fer leavin' us. I told him I was glad he ... he ... he never ended up in here. I ..." Suddenly, she broke into another heavy fit of coughing.

"She's gettin' worse," whispered Aggie. "Mary, what'll we do?"

Mary looked at her with tear-filled eyes. "Aggie, I don't know. Lily doesn't want us to get the Matron."

Aggie studied Lily. "Well, I don't care what she says. I'm goin' to." She rose. "Lily's son would need to be here." She began to cry. "Mary, she's dyin'. Her son would need to be with her."

"Aggie," gasped Lily. "Please. I won't be long now. I know it and I don't really mind. I'm ... I'm ... I'm happy to be goin'. I am, really." She turned to Mary. "But I'd be a lot happier goin' if ye promised me somethin', Mary."

"Oh, Lily," cried Mary. "Anythin'. Anythin'. Just ask."

"Thanks, Mary," smiled Lily, and her breathing seemed to ease. "I wanted to say that if yer son gets the letter, and he comes to get yees out, would ye ... would ye take Paul with yees? He's a good boy. He's suffered a lot. I wouldn't want him to be left all alone in here." She coughed a couple of times. "Mary, I know I'm askin' a lot of ye, but if ye could manage it?" She studied Mary, waiting for an answer.

Mary frowned, but she said, "Aye, Lily, I'll do me best fer Paul. But Eamon mightn't come. He mightn't even get the letter."

Lily smiled at her. Suddenly, she gasped and sat up. And with her eyes glistening, she stared past Mary. She smiled, then raised her hands and held them out. "Kevin," she whispered. "Lillian. Oh, ye've come fer me. Ye've come ... fer me..." and with a sigh, she breathed her last and fell back.

Aggie and Mary stared at her. "Oh, God, she's dead," cried Aggie. "Oh, God. She's dead!"

Crying, Mary ran from the ward to get the Matron.

THE PAUPERS' GRAVEYARD

That night, the Matron came for Paul. Jake, Davey and the boys nearest heard her say, "Carlin, yer mother's dead. Do ye want to see her before we put her into a bag fer burial?" She glared around the dormitory when she heard the gasps from Jake and some of the other boys. Jake felt angry at the way the Matron had broken the terrible news to Paul. "Come with me, then," snapped the Matron when Paul nodded. Jake studied Paul as he rose to his feet slowly and, without a word, followed the Matron out of the dormitory.

When he returned, Jake went to him. "Paul, I'm sorry fer yer trouble," he whispered.

Paul shrugged. "She's better off."

When Jake returned to bed, Davey whispered, "Is Paul all right?"

"Aye," whispered Jake. But he didn't think so.

***

It was around two in the morning when a noise woke the boys. Paul was on his feet, banging his head against the wall. Blood was pouring down his face and he was crying loudly. Scrambling to his feet, Jake went to him. "Paul," he whispered as he tried to stop him. "Come on, lie down. Lie down."

Paul turned. He stared stupidly at Jake. "Jake, there's no God," he said quietly. Jake frowned as he stared at the blood dripping off Paul's chin. "What?"

"There's no God," repeated Paul, allowing Jake to help him lie down. "Me ma always said there was, but she was lyin'." Jake studied Paul's face. He could see there was a small gash on his forehead, but he was not badly hurt. "There's no God," Paul kept repeating, over and over. Jake stayed by Paul's bed until he fell asleep.

***

Just beyond the wall of the Workhouse, Jake, Paul and another man, a gravedigger, were digging the hole in the muddy ground of the Paupers' Graveyard. Deep puddles of water covered the graveyard and the rain was cascading down the green, algae-covered Workhouse wall and seeping into the ground. The rain was so heavy that Jake couldn't tell if Paul was crying or not as he stared at his mother who was lying by the wall in a canvas bag that was tied at the top. As they dug, unearthing the bones of other inmates who had been buried there, their spades clogged with mud, but soon, under the gravedigger's directions, the grave was big and deep enough to take Lily's remains. Already there were about four inches of water at the bottom of the grave.

"I'll get help," said the gravedigger, and hurried away. He returned with another man a minute later and both men carried Paul's mother over to the edge of the grave and laid her down. Then the gravedigger turned to Paul, "Do ye want to say a few words over yer ma before we lower her down?"

"Words," muttered Paul. "What good are words now? She wouldn't hear them."

The gravedigger shrugged and was about to reach for the corpse when Jake said to Paul, "Would ye mind if I said somethin'?" Paul stared at the bag containing his dead mother and didn't answer. So, blessing himself, Jake said, "Jesus, please luk after the soul of Paul's mother, Lily. Amen." Then he blessed himself again.

"Right, Mick," said the gravedigger, "grab her feet."

The boys watched the two men slide Lily's body into the waterlogged grave, head first. A few seconds later, the four of them were spading the clay on top of the body. Jake stood with Paul until the men had gone inside. The rain grew heavier.

***

The noise woke Jake that night, and he blinked as he looked down the dormitory at the porter's assistant who carried an oil lamp. Reggie was holding Paul by one arm and was shouting, "Carlin, get back to bed and stay there! If the porter catches ye over the wall, he'll not be so lenient. Get to bed." With a curse, he flung Paul up the dormitory.

When Reggie was gone, Jake slipped over to his distraught friend. He was caked with mud. "Jake," cried Paul, the tears running down his face. "She floated to the top."

"What? Here, Paul, lie down," whispered Jake, wondering what he meant.

"She floated to the top," repeated Paul. "Oh, God, Jake, I tried to get her to stay down, but she kept floatin' to the top."

"What do ye mean?" asked Jake.

"I slipped out," cried Paul. "I wanted to say a prayer over her. When I got there ... oh, God," he cried. "Her head was stickin' out of the grave. She'd slipped out of the bag. There was water everywhere. She'd floated to the top." He began to cry louder. "She wouldn't stay down, Jake. She wouldn't. She'd floated to the top and I couldn't get her to stay down."

Jake gulped as the horror of what Paul had told him sank in. The water had filled Paul's mother's grave and she had slipped out of the bag and floated to the surface.

Suddenly, Paul tried to get to his feet, saying, "I have to go to her ..."

"No, Paul, ye can't. Ye'll only get in trouble if ye go over the wall," said Jake, restraining him. "Luk, ye might be able to see her in the mornin'. If ye go out again the night, ye'll only get in trouble."

"But she's floated to the top," said Paul, staring up at the roof. "She's floated to the top. She's lyin' in the muck."

When Jake woke in the morning, Paul was gone. He's slipped out again, he thought. At breakfast, he found out he was right.

When prayers were over, the Master glared around the hall. "In the middle of the night," he began, "a boy was caught outside the Workhouse wall. His name is Paul Carlin. Punishment fer goin' over the wall is a day in the Punishment Room. Let it be a lesson to all of ye, that anyone caught tryin' to leave the Workhouse without permission will spend a full day in the Punishment Room."

Jake ground his teeth as he looked at the Master. He must know why Paul went over the wall, he thought. There's no pity in him. Surely he could have let Paul off. He remembered now Davey's treatment by the Matron. Both their mothers were dead. Jake turned to look at his mother. She was standing with her head bowed. She looked pale and haggard, and Jake realised she looked thinner. He stifled a cry and so wanted to go to her and hug her, protect her, but he wasn't allowed to.

After breakfast, Reggie said to Jake, McCallister and another boy, "You three are to go out to the Paupers' Graveyard with the gravedigger and two of the men. The graves are waterlogged. Some of the bodies need to be reburied."

"Reburied?" exclaimed Jake.

"Aye," snapped the porter's assistant. "And this time, make sure they stay down."

It was still raining when the three boys and the men reached the gravesite. The horror that met them had Jake's stomach churning. There were bones strewn all over the site. Two skulls could be seen half-buried in the watery mud. On the far edge, where Paul's mother had been buried, two huge black rats were eating at something that looked to Jake like a hand. Several whole skeletons lay along the nearest edge of the graveyard. But it was Paul's mother, with her head sticking up out of the mud, that was the most horrifying sight. Shuddering, he turned away.

"We'll dig a pit over there," said the gravedigger. "The ground is harder near the wall."

An hour later, as Jake and McCallister went to lift a skeleton into a barrow to take it over to the pit to throw it in with the other bones, the cadaver suddenly broke in pieces and the bones rattled against the wet barrow as they fell. Jake stared at the arm bone he was left holding, and suddenly, his stomach heaved. With a croak, he vomited up his breakfast. McCallister grinned at him. "What's wrong, Miller?" he sneered. "Have ye never seen a bone before?"

Later, when the bones and other skeletons and bodies were buried, Jake and the others hurried to clean themselves up.

That night Jake thought about Paul. He hoped he was all right. His thoughts were interrupted by McCallister and his cronies, who had slipped up to him and Davey.

"We saw yer ma the day, O'Donnell," said McCallister.

Jake stared at him. What's he up to? he thought.

"What do ye mean?" asked Davey.

"McCallister, no!" shouted Jake, realising now what the bully was up to. He scrambled to his feet.

The bully ignored him. "She luked very pretty," he said. "I buried her head and Miller here buried the rest of her after he had a good vomit."

Davey frowned. "I don't ..."

"McCallister," said Jake reaching out. "I said *No!* Leave Davey alone."

"Jake, what does he mean?" asked Davey.

McCallister was determined to tell Davey. "Yer ma had ..."

Suddenly, Jake punched him. The blow landed right on the point of the bully's jaw and his eyes widened with shock as he collapsed onto his back near the wall. "I told ye to shut up, McCallister!" shouted Jake, trembling with anger as he glared at the bully. "Now get back to yer bed and leave Davey alone!"

McCallister rubbed his jaw. He looked at Doherty and the other two boys. "Get him," he grunted.

Jake took a step towards Doherty. Doherty studied him and then looked at McCallister, who had made no effort to get to his feet. "Get him yersel', McCallister," he snapped.

The bully glared at him and raised his fist in a threatening gesture, but Doherty glared back at him, unafraid.

"Did ye hear me, McCallister?" said Jake. "I told ye to get back to bed and leave Davey alone." He watched as Doherty and the other boys slipped away down the dormitory.

McCallister, seeing he had no back up, rose to his feet. "I'll get even with ye, Miller," he snarled.

"Aye, on yer own," sneered Jake, "yer nothin' but a coward, McCallister. On yer own, yer nothin'. Now, get back to yer bed!" With a scowl, McCallister backed away.

When Jake lay down again, Davey whispered, "Jake, what did he mean about me ma?"

"Ach, nothin', Davey," said Jake. "Ye know the kind of that gulpin'. He's a bully. He'll not harm us again. Don't ever be afraid of him."

"He said somethin' about me ma," whispered Davey, and Jake could hear by the tremble in Davey's voice he was ready to cry.

"He'll say anythin' to start a row, that gulpin'," said Jake. "Davey, don't worry about it. Go to sleep."

There was a moment's silence, then ... "Night, Jake."

"Aye. Night, Davey." Jake sighed silently. He was glad Davey didn't know about his mother. He shuddered as he remembered.

That night, Jake had a nightmare. He was standing in the moonlit Paupers' Graveyard, surrounded by skeletons. They all had their arms outstretched and were coming closer. Then Jake saw Paul's mother. The skin was almost stripped from her face, but he knew it was her. She was grinning horribly at him and, suddenly, she reached up and lifted her head off and rolled it towards him. Jake stared at it as it stopped at his feet. Lily's head was still grinning up at him.

He woke with a cry. Sweat bubbled on his face and he lay awake a long time thinking about Paul and his mother. He wondered what he would do if anything happened to his mother or his father.

Davey's Punishment

Just before breakfast, Paul was let out of the dark Punishment Room. As he joined the queue with the other boys, Jake studied him. Paul appeared not to notice they were there. He just stared at the floor as they moved quickly towards the table. Later, when they were eating, Jake whispered to him, "Paul, are ye all right?"

Paul stared at him. "All right?" he said quietly. "Aye, I'm all right." Then he ignored Jake and began to eat his porridge. Jake frowned. It was obvious Paul wasn't all right. Later that night he tried to speak with him again. But Paul just grunted and said little.

Over the next three days, Paul grew more withdrawn. He did his work in the yard, but hardly spoke to Jake or anyone.

The following night, Davey, slipping past his bed, woke Jake. He stared after the little boy and was about to ask him where he was going when he saw Davey stop at Paul's bed and shake him awake. Jake saw Paul sit up and he watched as the two of them whispered to each other for a few minutes. When Davey returned to bed, Jake pretended to be asleep. He was curious. What had Davey and Paul been talking about? Jake preferred to wait until either of them told him.

Next morning, Jake noticed Paul was almost his old self again. He realised that whatever Davey and Paul had been talking about was the reason. He wondered about it.

And so, Jake's life in the Derry Workhouse went on.

***

A few days after Christmas, Eamon returned home to find Ann in tears. He saw the letter in her hand and his heart began to pound. "What is it? Me da? Is he sick? Me ma? Jake? What is it? Ann ... what's happened?"

For a few seconds, Ann couldn't speak. Eamon cursed that he couldn't read. "Eamon, they're in the Derry Workhouse." She began to cry. The terrible shock of the news stunned him and he wasn't able to speak for a few seconds. "They had to go into the Workhouse because McConnell evicted them," explained Ann.

"Evicted! The bastard!" cried Eamon. "Oh, the bastard!" He sat down and buried his head in his hands. "Me ma ... Jake ... me da." Tears ran through his fingers as he sobbed bitterly. Ann knelt to hold him. Eamon looked at her with tear-filled eyes as he cried, "Ann, what are we goin' to do? I can't let them rot in that terrible place. Oh, God, they must hate me."

"Ah, no, Eamon ..."

"Aye, Ann. It was my fault, all my fault. If I hadn't emigrated they'd be all right. It's all my fault. I knew we'd have to pay fer the happiness we've found here. I knew it. Everythin' was goin' too well."

"Eamon, it isn't yer fault."

Eamon began to cry again. "Aye, Ann, it is. I should have stayed."

As the evening drew to a close, Eamon became more rational and they were soon discussing how they could help his family in Derry.

***

Two days before Easter, Jake, Paul and two of the bigger boys were told they would be making up a working party with six of the men. The working party was to be taken to a big house in Ballykelly, seventeen miles away, where they were to help dig out a long driveway and lay stones that had been delivered from the Workhouse over the past winter. The money that the boys and men would earn would go to buying food and linen and other necessities for the Workhouse.

Jake and the boys were excited; to them, leaving the Workhouse for even one day was like a holiday. Jake was glad

Paul had been picked, though he wondered why McCallister hadn't been chosen. He found out later McCallister had fallen foul of Reggie. The bully was in a terrible mood at missing the chance to join the working party.

At supper next evening, McCallister ground his teeth with anger when he heard Jake, Paul and the other boys whispering excitedly about their trip outside.

"I wish I was goin' with yees," whispered Davey.

"I'll tell ye all about it when we get back," said Jake, smiling.

McCallister, who by this time was unable to contain his anger, hissed, "Miller, did ye not tell O'Donnell about his ma?"

Jake froze. If they had been in the dormitory he would have punched McCallister to stop him, but he knew if he started a fight here, in front of the porter and the Master, he would jeopardise his place in the work party and probably be thrown into the Punishment Room. "McCallister!" he hissed, warning the bully to keep quiet.

But McCallister ignored him. "Yer ma was sittin' in the muck, O'Donnell," he whispered, glancing over at the porter's assistant.

"Muck?" said Davey. He frowned as he looked at Jake.

Jake hissed, "McCallister, I'm warnin' ye."

But the bully was determined to upset Davey. "We had to bury her again," he said. "She was all covered in muck. Aye, and her head was hangin' off." Davey stared at him as the bully continued. Jake could do nothing. "Me and Miller threw her into the pit with the other dead 'uns."

"McCallister!" shouted Jake as loud as he could. His shout drew Reggie's attention.

"Quiet over there!" Reggie hissed, glancing at the porter who was glaring over at them.

"What do ye mean," whispered Davey, "with the other dead 'uns?"

"McCallister," pleaded Jake. "Please ..."

The bully ignored him. "Yer ma and the other dead 'uns floated to the top of the muck and we had to bury her. Her head fell off as we carried her to the pit."

The boys nearest to Davey and Jake gasped as Davey's eyes widened with horror. "No," he muttered. Suddenly, he stood up. "No!" he screamed. "Yer lyin', McCallister! It isn't true. Yer lyin'!"

"Boy, sit down!" shouted Reggie.

But, screaming, Davey tried to scramble over the table to get at the bully. "Yer lyin'! Yer lyin'! Yer lyin' ..."

With a curse, Reggie grabbed him by the arm and hauled him off the table. As he did, the porter came over and, glaring at Davey, he snarled, "Yer fer the Punishment Room, boy."

At this threat, Davey stiffened and his eyes widened with fear. "No," he cried. "I'm sorry. Please ..."

"Sir," said Jake, "it wasn't Davey's fault."

Grabbing Jake by the arm, Reggie hissed, "Miller, I'd advise ye to keep yer mouth shut if ye want to go on the workin' party the morra."

"What is all this commotion?" Everyone froze. It was the Master.

"This boy was fightin', sir," said the porter. "He's fer the Punishment Room."

"Fightin'?" said the Master, studying the frightened little boy. "I will not tolerate fightin' in the Workhouse. Come here, boy." The boys held their breaths as the porter pushed Davey towards the Master. "Were ye fightin', boy?" asked the Master.

Crack! The sound of the Master slapping Davey silenced the hall and men, women and girls, everyone – frightened for the little boy – looked over. "I asked ye a question!" shouted the Master.

"No ... I ..." began Davey.

Crack! Jake clenched his fists when the Master slapped Davey again. "I asked, were ye fightin'?" shouted the Master.

Tears ran down Davey's pale face. The little boy was shocked. "No ... yes," he whispered. The sound of water dribbling onto the floor had the Master stepping back in disgust. Davey had wet himself.

"Take him out of me sight!" shouted the Master. Crying, Davey was hauled away by the porter and Reggie.

That night, Jake stood over McCallister. "Get up!" he said quietly. The bully stared at him. All the boys quickly gathered behind Jake. "McCallister," said Jake. "I'm goin' to give ye a hammerin'. And when I'm done, ye will go to the porter and tell him it was yer fault. Ye will tell him Davey wasn't fightin' and that it was you who started it."

McCallister shook his head. "Ye must think I'm an eejit," he said. "I won't."

With a grunt, Jake reached to haul McCallister to his feet, but as he did, the bully kicked at his face. The surprise blow caught Jake beneath his left cheekbone and he staggered back into the boys gathered behind him. They scattered when, with a bellow, McCallister jumped to his feet and dived at Jake, punching at him. Jake, though able to block most of the bully's blows, was still caught a couple of times. Although dazed, he saw McCallister's head in front of him and, with a yell, he punched the bully in the right eye. Still McCallister came on, for he knew if he stopped now, Jake would beat him. McCallister was smart enough to know that the best defence was attack and, lowering his head, he dived at Jake's stomach. But as he did so, Jake snapped up his knee suddenly and caught the bully square on the chin, throwing him back. In a second, Jake was into the bully, punching at his stomach as hard as he could until, with a gasp, McCallister fell to his knees.

Breathing hard, Jake stood over him. "Now ye'll go down to the porter's office, McCallister!" he shouted. "And ye'll tell him it was yer fault wee Davey was put in the Punishment Room. Ye hear me?" Suddenly, he hit McCallister in the other eye.

Putting his hands up in defeat, McCallister gasped, "Aye, aye. I'll do it. Don't hit me again. I'll do it. I'll go."

"Now!" shouted Jake. He hoped Davey was all right. "Get on yer feet." Slowly, McCallister stood up. "Go down now and tell the porter to let Davey out. Ye'll tell him that ye'll take Davey's place because it was yer fault."

McCallister gaped at him. "Me?"

"Aye!" shouted Jake. Whack! He thumped the bully again. "Now!" he shouted. "Or so help me, McCallister, I'll kill ye."

"I'll go. I'll go," cried the bully. "Just don't hit me again. I'll go." All the boys felt like cheering when they saw McCallister stumble across the dormitory to the door.

McCallister returned fifteen minutes later. "I told the porter," he said to Jake. "Honest." He raised his hands to his face, afraid Jake would strike him again. "I told him it was my fault, but the porter said O'Donnell will have to stay there 'til the mornin'. Matron has the key."

"McCallister," hissed Jake. "If yer lyin', I'll really lay into ye. I mean it."

"I'm not lyin'," said the bully. "Honest. The Matron has the key. The porter gave it to her. O'Donnell won't get out 'til the mornin'."

"Ye'd better not be lyin', McCallister."

"I'm not. Honest. I told him it was my fault."

Jake studied the bully. He believed him. Davey would have to stay the night in the Punishment Room. He prayed he would be all right.

Later, as he lay worrying about the little boy, he thought about his parents. He hadn't spoken to them in months. He saw them every day at mealtimes, but they were always kept apart. His mother often smiled across at him, but his father only glanced in his direction a few times. Jake wondered now how Eamon was. It seemed a lifetime since he had said goodbye to him on Derry Quay. He could hardly remember what his brother looked like. Jake was surprised to feel tears running down his face. He thought he was all cried out and he fell asleep thinking of the good times when they were all happy at the cottage.

Rebellion

At breakfast, Jake looked for the Matron. Her assistant had brought out the women, but there was no sign of her. After breakfast, Jake didn't have any time to question Reggie before they were led out to the waiting horse and cart. At the bottom of the thirteen steps, the men and the boys loaded picks, sledgehammers, spades, shovels and four barrows onto the cart.

As the horse and cart carried them towards the main road to Ballykelly, Jake looked back at the Workhouse; he thought now that if his parents hadn't been in the Workhouse, it would have been a great opportunity to run away. He was stronger now and he reckoned he could survive on his own. He turned to look at Paul. His friend was quiet as he looked ahead. "We're out of that place fer a day, thank God," said Jake. "Maybe two, if we're lucky."

Paul turned. "Aye, if we're lucky," he said. Jake didn't know it, but Paul had decided that as soon as he got a chance he would go on the run. His mother was dead. There was nothing to hold him in the Workhouse. The Workhouse had been his life ever since he could remember. The three people he loved had died there and he was determined he would not.

They reached Ballykelly three hours later. Seven hillock-high piles of stones greeted them as the cart turned into a marked-out, winding driveway. The way up to the big house on the hill was set out with wooden pegs and twine. "It'll take more nor a couple of days to dig that driveway and hard-core it," muttered one of the men.

Just then, a stout, red-faced man, wearing a tweed coat and corduroy trousers, came hurrying down to them. "Ye'll find more barrows and spades lying by the big shed at the back of the main house," said the man, obviously the owner of the land. "My men have begun the top of the drive. You lot can start here. I want all the ground inside the pegs dug down to the hard clay."

"Right, Mr Gilliland," said one of the men who knew him.

By six-thirty, when it was almost dark, the boys and men were exhausted. Nearly three quarters of the drive had been dug. But it was another half-hour before they were being led to a barn behind the outhouse to get fed. The barn was lit by three oil lamps, and Mrs Gilliland, a plump woman with her hair tied in a bun, wearing an apron, stood with her daughter, a ten-year-old with dark hair in ringlets, dishing out stew from a huge black cauldron. The Workhouse inmates' mouths began to water as they queued up to be served.

Later, when they were eating, Mr Gilliland came into the barn. "Eat yer fill," he said. "Ye'll have porridge in the mornin' as well. I want all of the driveway dug and most of the stones laid before the morra night." He studied the inmates. "Yer Master said yees would work hard and ye have done well so far." He pointed to the loft. A wooden ladder led up to it. "Ye'll be warm sleepin' up there. There's plenty of hay."

That night before going to sleep, Jake said to Paul, "I hope wee Davey is all right."

"He's a nice wee fella," said Paul.

"Aye."

"Jake, when I got out of the Punishment Room, I was sort of away in me head," said Paul suddenly. "Me ma was dead. I wanted to die too. Wee Davey came over to me one night. He said not to be so sad. He said he missed his ma, but he said she told him never to be afraid because he would see her again. At first, I didn't want to hear what he was sayin', but I listened to him. Here was this wee fella tellin' me not to be sad. His mother had died in the Workhouse too. It was harder on him than it was on me. He's only wee."

Jake smiled. "I understand, Paul. We'll have to cheer him up when we get back. At least by now he'll be out of the Punishment Room."

"Aye," said Paul. He frowned as he thought, I owe wee Davey. He couldn't leave him alone. They had to help him. He sighed. He could still run away, but not yet. There would be other opportunities later, and he would take the first one.

Jake slept easy that night. He had enjoyed the hard work away from the Workhouse. Out in the open countryside he had felt happy.

The rooster's call in the morning woke them. It was a warm Easter morning and they woke groaning. Muscles they hadn't used for a long time ached. A few minutes after waking, Mrs Gilliland and her daughter came in carrying a pot with steaming porridge. Mr Gilliland came in as they were eating. "There's fresh milk outside," he said. "We'll begin work in ten minutes."

By the end of the day, almost all the drive was finished. Mr Gilliland told them he had estimated that it would be around dinnertime next day before the work would be completed.

At three-fifteen the following day they were on their way back to the Workhouse. As Jake climbed the thirteen steps, he thought about Davey.

Reggie led the boys and the men out to the yard to break rocks until suppertime.

At supper, Jake looked for Davey as the other boys joined the queue. He frowned. Where is he? As they sat down to eat, Jake whispered to McCallister, "McCallister, where's Davey?" McCallister frowned and then suddenly gasped. Jake stared at him. "Where's Davey?" he repeated, his heart beating faster.

"I ... I don't know," said McCallister.

"What do ye mean ye don't know?" asked Jake. He could feel the hair creep along the nape of his neck. Something was wrong.

"Miller," whispered McCallister, glancing at Reggie. "I think O'Donnell is still in the Punishment Room."

"Still!" gasped Jake. Rising, he went over to Reggie.

"Miller, what are ..." began the porter's assistant.

"Did Davey get out of the Punishment Room?" asked Jake. "Davey?"

"O'Donnell," said Jake. "Was he let out of the Punishment Room?"

Reggie stared at him. Slowly, he stood up. "I ... I think he's still in ..."

"What!" exclaimed Jake. "Ye fergot about him! Ye fergot about him!" he shouted when he saw the look on Reggie's face.

Immediately, Reggie hurried over to the porter and Jake watched, his heart pounding as the two men conversed. Then the porter rose and, followed by Reggie, they hurried out of the dining hall. Jake followed them to the Punishment Room. Banging on the door, the porter shouted, "O'Donnell, can ye hear me? O'Donnell!"

"Let him out!" shouted Jake. "Get the key!"

"I don't have it," said the porter. "The Matron has it. She took it with her when she went on her Easter break."

"But Davey's been in there fer three days!" cried Jake. "Oh God. Oh God ... three days. Break down the door!"

"Break down the door?" exclaimed the porter. "I can't do that. I'll need to see the Master."

"Well go and see him!" shouted Jake. "Hurry!"

The porter glared at him. "Miller, get back to the dinin' hall. I'll sort this out." Then he hurried away.

Jake glared at Reggie. Then he banged on the door. "Davey! Davey, can ye hear me? It's Jake. We'll have ye out soon. Don't worry. Don't worry!" Jake thought about his own time in the Punishment Room. He hadn't been able to hear any sound from outside the room. All he'd heard had been the rat scuffling and its screeches. The rat! "Davey!" he screamed, banging on the door. "Davey!"

"Miller," snapped Reggie, grabbing him by the shoulder. "Ye heard the porter. Get back to the dinin' hall."

Jake turned to him. The porter's assistant almost gasped aloud at the look on Jake's face as he said coldly, "I'm not goin' anywhere 'til Davey is out of there."

"Are ye still here, Miller?" snapped the porter on his return.

"What did the Master say?" asked Jake.

"He said to leave O'Donnell in there 'til the morra mornin'. When the Matron comes, she'll let him out. Now get back to ..."

"He said to leave Davey in there?" exclaimed Jake, unable to believe it was true. "But he's been in there three days."

The porter shrugged. "He'll be all right. I've seen boys locked up there fer a couple of days. They were hungry when they got out, but they were all right."

"But Davey's only wee ..."

"Lissen, Miller, get back to the dinin' hall and finish yer supper and no more about this. O'Donnell will get out in the mornin'."

"Naw," said Jake, looking at the door. "He'll get out now." With that, he turned and hurried to the dining hall. The porter and his assistant stared after him.

Paul and the other boys gathered around Jake. The women, girls and men, curious, stared over at them. "Paul," said Jake. "Davey's been in the Punishment Room since we went to Ballykelly; three days. The Matron has the key, but she won't be back 'til the mornin'. The Master won't allow the porter to break down the door." He turned and looked at McCallister. "Davey'll die, McCallister. If he has to spend another night in there, he'll die. God knows what he's like now. He was afraid of that room."

"Well, what do ye want me to do about it?" snapped McCallister.

"Help me break open the door," said Jake, looking at the other boys. "All of yees. They can't stop us all. We have to get wee Davey out. If we don't, he'll die. He'll die!"

"But what about the Master?" exclaimed Doherty.

"He can't stop us all," said Jake.

"I'm with ye, Jake," said Paul, turning to the other boys. "What about the rest of yees?"

"I'm not," said a fair-haired boy. "The Master will punish us if we do any damage to the Workhouse."

McCallister frowned. It was his fault Davey was in the Punishment Room in the first place. Suddenly, he turned to the boy who had spoken last. "What can he do to us? Nothin'. He can't throw us *all* in the Punishment Room, can he?"

Jake stared at him. Was this the McCallister he once hated?

"What if *you* were left in the Punishment Room fer three days?" McCallister shouted at the boy. "Ye'd want us to get ye out, wouldn't ye? Well, wouldn't ye?" He glared around at the other boys. Some of them were nodding in agreement. "Well, come on then," said McCallister. "Some of ye come with me. We'll get a few bars and a pick and a sledge. We'll soon have O'Donnell out of there. Come on!"

"We'll get round to the Punishment Room," said Jake. "Meet us there." He smiled at McCallister. McCallister nodded, then hurried off, followed by Doherty and four other boys.

Everyone in the hall gaped as Jake led the other boys to the Punishment Room. Mary looked across at Paddy. He frowned and she said a quick prayer.

THE SHINING CHILDREN

When Jake and the boys came running to the Punishment Room, Reggie and the porter were astonished.

"Where do ye think yer goin'?" shouted the porter. "Get back to the dinin' hall at once!"

"Naw. We're here to let Davey out!" shouted Jake.

Just then, McCallister and the other boys appeared at the end of the corridor. McCallister, carrying a pick over his shoulders, was leading the way. Behind him, Doherty carried a huge crowbar. Two other boys were trailing big sledgehammers after them.

"Who told ye ye could take those tools from the yard, McCallister?" shouted Reggie when they gathered beside Jake and the others. Reggie and the porter studied the boys. They could see they were in a determined mood.

"Luk," said the porter. "If yees go back to the dormitory now, nothin' more will be said about this. O'Donnell will be let out in the mornin'."

"Naw," said Jake, reaching to take a crowbar from Doherty. We're freein' Davey now." The porter moved to block his way. "Out of me way!" shouted Jake, glaring at him as he gripped the crowbar tighter. But the porter held his ground.

Suddenly McCallister dropped the pick and grabbed the porter by the lapels of his coat and hauled him to one side. Doherty and another boy rushed to help McCallister and together they restrained the red-faced, struggling porter. At this, Reggie grew frightened and took off down the corridor, yelling, "Master! Help! Master! Master!"

Still struggling, the porter shouted, "Yees'll be sorry fer this! Let me go! Let ... me ... go!"

Ignoring him, Jake forced the flat end of the crowbar between the edge of the door and the doorjamb. "Paul, help me," he grunted as he levered it. McCallister watched as Jake and Paul hauled on the crowbar. Suddenly, it snapped away. They tried again, but the same thing happened.

"Here," said McCallister to Doherty and the other boy. "Houl' onto him and give me that pick!"

As Jake and Paul jammed the crowbar into the joint again, McCallister placed the pointed end of the pick into the joint about halfway up the door. "Hand me one of those sledges," said McCallister. Using the sledge, he tapped the other end of the pick until it was firmly jammed into the door joint. "Carlin, houl' onto the crowbar," he said. Jake helped Paul hold the crowbar level. McCallister then tapped the end of it until it, too, was jammed tight. "Now!" said McCallister, grabbing the pick handle. Jake and Paul gripped the end of the crowbar and, together, the three boys hauled hard. Suddenly, with a loud crack, the hinges and the lock yielded to the pressure and the door crashed open. Handing the crowbar to Paul, Jake then rushed into the Punishment Room. Davey was lying curled into a ball against the far wall.

Dropping to his knees beside him, Jake cried, "Davey. Oh, God, Davey." Lifting Davey into his arms, he held him close. He was shocked at how light the tiny boy was. Davey's trousers were soaked in urine.

"Jake," gasped Davey and smiled. His teeth looked oddly huge on his chalk-white face. "I knew ye'd come and get me out."

Tears ran down Jake's face as he studied Davey. The little boy's cheekbones jutted hard against his skin. "Davey," sniffed Jake, "we'll get ye somethin' to eat. Yer goin' to be all right."

"Jake," whispered Davey, suddenly swallowing so Jake could hardly hear him.

"Aye?" he whispered back. "What is it?"

"It came," whispered the little boy, suddenly trembling.

"What?" asked Jake, knowing what Davey was going to say.

"The rat. It came. And ... and, Jake, it was really big, really big. I was afraid at first, but," he smiled, "then they came."

Jake frowned. "They? Who are ye talkin' about, Davey?" he asked, thinking, he's ravin'.

"The children," answered Davey, "and there was a whole lot of them, all shinin'."

"Shinin'?"

"Aye. They told me not to be afraid," whispered Davey, swallowing again as he tried to speak clearly. "They told me everythin' would be all right. Jake," he gasped, "ye should have seen them. They were lovely. I've never seen anythin' as lovely as they were."

His head's gone, thought Jake. He doesn't know what he's sayin'. "Come on, Davey," he whispered. "I'll get ye out of here."

"Oh, Jake, no. Let me stay just a wee while longer. Please," whispered Davey.

Jake frowned. "Stay?"

"Just another wee while longer. They might come back, ye see. Oh, Jake, I want to see them again. I want to ..."

"But ye can't stay here, Davey. Come on. I'll carry ye back to bed. We'll get ye somethin' to eat first, and then ye can sleep." Jake's heart pounded. Davey wasn't well. He straightened.

When Jake, carrying Davey, came out of the Punishment Room, the other boys gathered around them. Some of them had tears in their eyes when they saw the condition little Davey was in. Just then, the Master and Reggie arrived, and, immediately, the boys restraining the porter released him.

"What have yees done?" shouted the Master, staring at the door. "Yees have damaged Workhouse property!"

"Aye, and we've saved Davey," shouted Jake. "Now get out of me way. We're takin' Davey to the dinin' hall to get him somethin' to eat. Then we're takin' him to the dorm to sleep."

"Yer goin' nowhere, Miller!" snapped the Master, pushing through the boys to stand in front of Jake. He studied the pathetic-looking, shivering boy in Jake's arms.

"Jake," whispered Davey, "I'll be all right. I'm just a bit cold, that's all. But I'll be all right. The children said not to be afraid. I'm not." He smiled.

"Put that boy down! Now!" shouted the Master, suddenly reaching towards Davey.

The look Jake gave him stopped the Master as he shouted, "If ye so much as touch Davey, I'll kill ye, ye bastard. Ye hear me, I'll kill ye! Now get out of me way!"

Shocked, the Master looked around at the other boys. He could see that not one of them was afraid of him now. Dazed, he stepped aside and the boys followed Jake up the corridor to the dinin' hall.

In the hall, Jake laid Davey gently on top of one of the tables and then said to Paul, "Would ye see if ye can get Davey a cup of buttermilk, Paul?" When Paul hurried away, the other boys gathered around Davey.

"Jake," whispered Davey, who seemed unaware of the others. "I wish ye could have seen them."

Jake glanced at McCallister, who quietly whispered, "Who's he talkin' about?"

At the sound of the bully's voice, Davey frowned and turned to look up at him. "They said ye wouldn't scare me again either."

McCallister frowned. "But I ... I didn't ..."

"Jake, they said that I was goin' with them," said Davey, turning to him. "Jake," he groaned suddenly, "I'm sore ... I'm so sore. Ughh!"

"Davey," cried Jake, "take it easy. Don't talk. We'll get ye to bed soon."

"Jake," said Davey, "don't ... don't worry about the rat any more if yer put into the Punishment Room again. It's gone. The children chased it away. It's gone and it won't be back."

Jake studied the little boy. "Davey," he whispered, "who are these children yer talkin' about? Where did they come from?"

Davey's answer shocked him. "From here," he whispered. "They're boys and girls who once lived here."

"Lived?" whispered Jake, looking at McCallister.

Suddenly, Davey groaned and turned sideways to look past Jake. Then he smiled and his face seemed to glow as he gasped, "Jake, they're here. They've come fer me. Can't ye see them? Oh, they've come fer me." Gasping for air, he tried to rise but he was so weak he couldn't. "Jake, see, there they are. Aren't

111

they so ... so ... beaut ... Jake ..." Suddenly, he gave a little sigh and his body just seemed to relax as his head rolled to one side and he was gone.

"Davey!" cried Jake. "Davey!"

Paul had just returned with the cup of buttermilk, and when he realised Davey was dead, he, too, began to cry.

Suddenly, McCallister gave an anguished cry. "I'm sorry, Davey. Oh, God, I'm so sorry. Fergive me. I didn't mean to hurt ye. Fergive me. Fergive me ..." And, bending over Davey's body, he reached to hug him close, all the time crying bitterly.

One of the boys said, "We'd better tell the porter."

"Aye," whispered Jake, suddenly feeling so tired, for all the fight had gone out of him.

Minutes later, the Master, porter and Reggie came into the dining hall. The Master studied the boys. He could see the change in them. They were subdued. I'll soon put them in their place, he thought as he shouted, "Get to bed! All of yees! Now!"

***

As Jake lay awake thinking about Davey, he wondered about the children Davey thought he had seen. Aye, he must have been out of his head, Jake thought. But now, Davey's words came to him. *"Jake, don't worry about the rat any more if yer put into the Punishment Room again. It's gone. The children chased it away. It's gone."* Now Jake began to cry for Davey, for his parents, for Eamon and Ann, and for himself.

***

At breakfast next morning, the Master, as usual, came out to say prayers. The Matron was there. Before speaking, the Master smiled at her and she smiled back. The Master began. "Last night, one of the boys passed away, an accident ..."

As he continued, Jake glared at him. McCallister's face was flushed with anger, too, but they said nothing.

The Master concluded by saying, "We will say a prayer fer the unfortunate boy." He smiled again at the Matron, who

112

stood with the key of the Punishment Room and other keys hanging by her side. She looked towards the boys, and when she moved, the keys rattled. Every boy there glared at her, their hatred of the hard woman almost thick enough to cut through. And through it all, the banging as the workmen repaired the Punishment Room door echoed around them.

At dinnertime, the Master sent Reggie to bring Jake and Paul to his office. The porter and the Matron were there when Jake and Paul arrived. "I am led to understand you two were the ringleaders in charge of that rebellion last night," said the Master, standing by his desk beside the Matron. He studied Jake, who stared straight at him, his head held high. "Matron, the porter and I have discussed what has happened and I am prepared to overlook the damage done to Workhouse property and the injuries inflicted on the porter. The door has been repaired. As I said, I am prepared to overlook everythin' if not a word of what happened to the unfortunate O'Donnell leaves this building."

Jake clenched his fists but said nothing. Paul glanced at him.

"Have I yer word, Miller?" asked the Master. "And yers, Carlin?"

Jake looked at the Matron and she smirked as if to say, ye'd better do as he says. That smirk was enough to trigger Jake's anger.

"Aye!" he shouted suddenly. "Ye have me word that if I can get anyone outside this hellhole to lissen to me, I'll tell them ye murdered wee Davey. Aye, yees murdered him," he repeated as the Matron gaped at him and the Master glanced at her. "The cruelty yees have showed to poor Davey and everyone in here will be known."

Suddenly, Jake could not control himself. In a second, he had reached the Master and his fist exploded against his chin. With a surprised croak, the Master staggered back and fell to the floor. The Matron cowered back as Jake glared at her, deciding whether to strike her as well. The Master stayed on the floor until Reggie and the porter had restrained Jake and, when he felt safe, he scrambled to his feet, screaming, "Take them to the Punishment Room! Lock them in!" Blood spat from his mouth as he screamed, "Ye'll rot in there, Miller. Ye'll rot before I let ye out again!"

As the Punishment Room door slammed behind them, Jake said, "Paul, I'm sorry. It was my fault."

"Ah, how was it?" said Paul. "Jesus, I wish I had taken a crack at the wee bastard. Ye nearly knocked his wee head off." He began to laugh. Jake giggled, and all of a sudden, he was laughing too.

But soon they realised what their punishment was. They knew they were in the Punishment Room to stay. The Master would see to it. He couldn't afford to let any word of what happened to Davey get out. If it did, he'd be finished. If Jake and Paul died in the Punishment Room, it would be seen as another 'accident'. No-one in the Workhouse would ever dare speak of how they died. They were in the Punishment Room to die.

THE STRANGER

Five days later, Jake and Paul were huddled together, hardly able to speak. Time had no meaning for Jake and Paul now, and those five days could have been five weeks. By then, they were too weak to even stand up, and they woke occasionally to just stare into the darkness. Jake often thought about the rat and Davey telling him the children had chased it away. It hadn't appeared.

By the sixth day, Jake couldn't get a word out of Paul. His friend was hardly breathing and he was terrified that Paul was dying. Jake couldn't cry any more. They both had cried together, coming to the conclusion that to die wouldn't be so bad – it would be better than spending the rest of their lives in the Workhouse anyway.

That night, Jake let go of Paul, too weak to hold onto him any longer, and fell back. As he lay drifting in and out of sleep and trying to catch his breath, he heard a voice. It was barely audible and, at first, Jake thought it was Paul. "Hold on, Jake," said the voice. "Don't give up."

"What?" croaked Jake, blinking into the darkness as something began to glow in the corner of the room.

"Don't give up, Jake," the voice repeated, and now Jake recognised it. It was Davey.

"Davey," he gasped.

"Hold on. Just a wee while longer."

The glow grew more defined and now Jake saw him. It *was* Davey. And behind him he saw the smiling faces, the shining faces, of other children. "Davey!" he cried. "Help us! Help us!"

Davey smiled. "Just a wee while longer," he said, the sound of his voice growing quieter. Then he began to fade.

"Davey! Come back!" shouted Jake. "Davey!" But he was gone. The darkness seemed even darker now. What did he mean?

thought Jake. Hold on? What does that mean? Hold on fer what? He grew angry. It was his imagination. How could it have been Davey? Davey was dead. Dead. He began to cry, a hopeless despairing cry, until he drifted once more into the peacefulness of sleep.

**

Jake's mother lay awake. She had hardly slept from the day she found out Jake and Paul had been put in the Punishment Room. She had asked to see the Master several times, but he had refused to see her. Mary knew Paddy, too, had tried to get to see the Master. Neither of them realised that the Master intended to leave Jake and Paul in the Punishment Room until they starved to death. Jake's parents believed that Jake and Paul were being fed and that surely they would be out soon.

**

Around eight o'clock next morning, the Master had a visitor. It was a tall, tanned stranger. As he studied him, he frowned. There was something familiar about the man.

"Sir. I believe ye have a family by the name of Miller stayin' here. I'd like to see them, if ye don't mind," said the stranger.

It was then the Master realised who the man looked like – the boy, Miller. "And who, might I ask, are you?" he snapped.

"Eamon Miller, sir. I am Mary and Patrick Miller's eldest son. Jake Miller's brother."

"Their … son? But they told me they had no other relations," exclaimed the Master. He could hear his heart pounding.

"Yeah, well, I am their son. Now, if I could see them," said Eamon. A nerve moved on the side of his face, for he was tired and irritable. It had been a long journey and he had arrived in Derry early that very morning and had come straight to the Workhouse. His passage from America had been arranged by Jack Cartwright, who had told Eamon that he and his wife would look after Ann and the babies until he returned. At first, Eamon had thought about sending James, his old friend back in

Ireland, the money to get his family out of the Workhouse. But he knew that his parents and Jake belonged in America with him and Ann. It was decided, by himself, Ann and the Cartwrights, that he should go back to Derry and, if he had to, he would carry his father to the ship and bring them all back to America with him.

"No," snapped the Master. "Ye cannot see them. I do not allow visitors into the Londonderry Workhouse. The Millers have stated, in writin', that they have no relatives. I believe them. I do not know what other purpose has brought ye here, but ye will not see them. Now, get out. Porter! Porter!" At once, the porter came rushing into the room. "Remove this ... this person from the Workhouse!" shouted the Master.

Eamon turned. He sized up the porter. He was around the same height. "Put a hand on me," he said quietly, "and I'll break it." Turning back to the Master, he said, "And if I don't get to see me ma and da and me brother, I'll wring yer scrawny neck fer ye. Do ye hear me?" he shouted. "Now do I get to see them, or do I have to go to the authorities?"

The Master spluttered. He was more afraid of the authorities than Eamon. The porter hadn't moved. He was afraid of Eamon.

"I said, do I get to see them?" said Eamon quietly, his dark eyes fixed on the Master.

The Master knew he was beaten and nodded to the porter. As Eamon and the porter left, the Master thought, perhaps if the Millers leave here, all this will blow over. But he knew it wouldn't. He hoped now, for his sake, that Jake was alive.

Eamon studied his father when the porter showed him to the garden. He was horrified at his father's condition. His father had his back to Eamon and the porter as he dug the clay at the edge of a cabbage patch. The porter watched as Eamon walked towards Paddy.

"Da," said Eamon quietly. His father stopped digging and frowned, but then continued to dig. "Da, it's me," said Eamon, reaching to touch his father on his left shoulder.

Eamon's father turned. At first, he couldn't believe it. He had thought often about Eamon and wondered how he was getting on. Many a time he regretted he had not said a proper goodbye to him. "Eamon!" he cried now as his son reached to hug him.

"I'm sorry, da. I'm so very sorry," cried Eamon.

Later, when they parted and Eamon explained why he had come, his father asked, "Does yer mother know?"

"Not yet. I haven't seen her. I've only just arrived. Come on," said Eamon smiling. "Let's get her. I'm takin' yees outta here."

***

The crash as the door opened woke Jake, and he stared up at the dark figures in the brightness of the doorway.

"Jake! Oh my God, Jake!" a familiar voice cried.

Jake stared at him. "Naw," he croaked, cowering against the wall, "it's not you. It's not Eamon! It's not ..."

"Aye, it's our Eamon, Jake," whispered his mother. She almost broke down when she saw her son's condition. She could see grey flecks in his greasy hair. "He's come all the way from America to take us ... take us all ... out of here. Oh, Jake," she cried.

Gently, Eamon lifted his brother into his strong arms to carry him out of the Punishment Room. As they came out into the corridor, Jake remembered about Paul. "Eamon," he gasped. "Paul. See if he's all right. I think he's ... he's dead." He began to cry.

Seconds later, Jake's mother and father were carrying Paul out of the room and gently laying him on the floor. Mary examined him. "He's breathin'," she said. "He's very weak, but I think he'll be all right. Ye'll both be all right," she added with a smile as the tears tripped down her happy face.

As Eamon carried Jake along the corridor, Jake asked, "Eamon, where are we goin'?"

His brother smiled. "First of all, I'm goin' to get yees fed and washed, and then you, me and me ma and da are goin' to book our passage to Philadelphia." He looked at his father. "Ye are comin', da, aren't ye?"

Paddy looked at Mary. "Aye," he said, tears filling his eyes. "I'm comin' with ye."

"Good," said Eamon. As they came up to the Master's office, Jake saw the Master and the Matron standing outside. "When I get yees fed," said Eamon, glaring at the Master, "I'm going to report this to the authorities and get them to investigate the cruelty in this place."

"And tell them about Davey," said Jake, looking at the Master as they walked past him. The Master and Matron stared after them for a few seconds, then, with a curse, the Master turned and went into his office. The Matron followed.

As they came to the doorway to walk out of the Workhouse, Jake turned to look back for the last time. Then, as his brother carried him down the thirteen steps, he smiled. He was out of hell. They were all out of hell.

The Master stood for a few seconds, looking down at his desk. His fists were clenched tight and sweat bubbled on his wrinkled white brow. He felt faint and sick, and his stomach was churning with fear. Suddenly, he reached and pulled the top drawer away from the desk and emptied the contents onto the top of it.

"Do ye think the Millers will really tell the authorities?" asked the Matron, wondering what the Master was doing.

The Master glared at her, his face twisted with anger. "Of course they will, ye stupid cow!" he shouted. Then he bent to pull out another drawer.

"There's no need to be so ... what are ye doin'?" asked the Matron.

"I'm clearin' out me desk," snapped the Master. "What does it luk like?"

"Clearing out yer desk? Why?"

"Are ye stupid, woman?" roared the Master. "Ye'll be lucky, no, we'll be lucky, we don't end up in prison over O'Donnell's death. I'm resignin' and I'd advise ye to do the bloody same."

"Resign? But ... we've a good job here," whined the Matron. "Anyway, who's goin' to believe the Millers over us?"

The Master straightened. "Woman, do ye understand what ye've done?"

"Me?"

"Aye, you. Ye've killed one of the inmates."

"But ..."

"Killed him!" shouted the Master. "And don't think the boy Miller will ferget it either. They'll tell, all right, and the best we can do is resign and get out."

"But ..."

"Woman, I'm busy. Now, get out of me sight!" he shouted. The Matron stared at him but didn't move. "I said get OUT!" roared the Master. In a second, he had rounded the desk, grabbed the shocked Matron by the arm, opened the door, and propelled her through it into the hall.

Standing in the hall were McCallister, Doherty and several other boys. They had heard everything. They laughed when they saw the Matron come flying out of the Master's office to hit the far wall. Hearing them laugh, the Matron turned to glare at them and, as she did, the boys' laughter grew louder. The Matron knew then they weren't afraid of her. With a snort, she turned to walk away. As she did, Doherty ran forward and gave her a good hard kick in the behind. With a cry, the Matron fled down the hall, the boys' laughter echoing behind her.

The boys had a leader in McCallister now. One they could respect. Maybe now that they, too, had a new power, their lives inside the Workhouse would get easier. The Master and the Matron would have to be replaced. Jake and his family would make sure of that. The authorities would make sure there would be no more cruelty in the Derry Workhouse.

Later, as they walked back to the dormitory, McCallister thought about wee Davey. He was determined never to be like his father. As long as he lived in the Workhouse, no boy would be bullied again. He would see to it. He smiled now as he thought about Jake and Paul. They had got out of the Workhouse. And someday he, too, might get out.

Epilogue

Slowly, the ship carried them away from Derry, and as it did, the Millers knew they could survive anything. They had a strength born from the Workhouse that would stand them well in America.

As the ship rounded the bend, and Derry disappeared for ever, Jake walked over to Paul, who was standing at the front of the ship looking out over the river. Jake had a new brother now. The bond between them was strong and would never be broken. In America they would live the lives they were destined for. And when they married and had children of their own, they would tell them all about their time in the Derry Workhouse. Their children would be proud of them and some day, perhaps, Jake or Paul's descendants would visit Derry to see the Workhouse for themselves.